BORN TOGETHER

BORN TOGETHER

THE STORY OF CONJOINED TWINS

MICHAEL L COX

The Book Guild Ltd

First published in Great Britain in 2020 by
The Book Guild Ltd
9 Priory Business Park
Wistow Road, Kibworth
Leicestershire, LE8 0RX
Freephone: 0800 999 2982
www.bookguild.co.uk
Email: info@bookguild.co.uk
Twitter: @bookguild

Typeset in 12pt Adobe Jenson Pro

Printed and bound by TJ International Ltd, Padstow, Cornwall

ISBN 978-1-913208-52-3

British Library Cataloguing in Publication Data.

A catalogue record for this book is available from the British Library.

MIX
Paper from
responsible sources
FSC® C013056

In the preparation of this book I wish to acknowledge help from various libraries and other sources but especially to the William Harvey Library at the George Eliot Hospital, NHS Trust and its staff, Stephen Ayre (Manager) and Beverley Wright (Senior Library Assistant).

Regards,
Michael

Contents

Introduction

My interest in multiple births, and especially conjoined twins, has developed through several events. The final result is this book, in which I present a comprehensive review of conjoined twins: their history, frequency, types, causes, medical aspects, psychology, ethics, appearances in mythology, fiction and entertainment, and not forgetting that animals can also be affected.

The first event that interested me was the birth in 1934 of the Dionne quins, all girls (not conjoined), in Canada. Although I was only five at the time, I remember the considerable public interest. Most extraordinary was the fact that they were born without the assistance of any doctor or midwife. In spite of this they all survived to adulthood.

The next event was the birth in 1948 by Caesarean section of the Good quads, all girls (not conjoined), at Southmead Hospital in Bristol, UK. Two of them were identical. For many years paediatrician Dr Beryl Corner continued a close interest in them. One of them died aged thirty-six. The other three celebrated their sixtieth birthday at Southmead in 2008.

A few years later, as a medical student, I learnt to deliver babies at that same hospital.

The next event occurred in 1953 when conjoined twin girls were brought from Nigeria to be separated in London by eminent surgeon Professor Ian Aird. This was probably the first such operation performed in Britain. One of the twins survived the surgery and was called Boko. She was still alive and well in 2015 at the age of sixty-two. Her story is told in Chapter 6.

A few years later I worked as a doctor in Nigeria, where I found that multiple pregnancy was much more common than in Europe or America. Their frequency in the Yoruba tribe, with whom I spent some time, may be the highest in the world. However, I never saw conjoined twins in that country. There is more about this in Chapter 9.

The final event that stimulated my interest occurred after I had returned to England from Nigeria and had become a consultant obstetrician and gynaecologist. A set of conjoined twins was delivered under my care. They are described in Chapter 6.

My experiences therefore led to a closer study of the subject, which resulted in a lecture about conjoined twins that I gave in 2003 to the Royal College of Obstetricians and Gynaecologists (RCOG). It was awarded the RCOG/Wyeth Historical Lecture Prize for that year.

What do surviving conjoined twins think about publicity such as is provided by this book? Is it intrusive voyeurism? In a detailed discussion of this topic, Alice Dreger points out the difference between being exhibited to medical personnel for the purposes of scientific study and exhibition to the public. In times past, exhibition was the only way such persons with abnormal bodies could earn a living. They were often exploited by showmen. Sometimes medical and public inspection could be combined, as when publicity included the information that doctors had confirmed and described detailed intimate anatomical details. Such was the case with Millie and Christine (see Chapter 3), where the publicity linked to medical details tried to avoid a charge of lewdness or pornography. Millie and Christine's theme song included words that suggest the combination of a certain pride together with optimism:

Two heads, four arms, four feet,
All in one perfect body meet,
I am most wonderfully made
All scientific men have said.

Today, as far as can be ascertained, some conjoined twins even welcome publicity. Exploitation, common in the past, must clearly be avoided. When discussing conjoined twins, Alice Dreger commented, "I began asking people with unusual anatomies how they felt when they appeared on the [chat] shows, and nearly all of them found it an extremely positive, even empowering experience. Having been taught to hide their 'shameful' anatomical difference, they saw such shows as an opportunity to be 'out' and proud of who they are. They were treated by host and audience as authorities on an important experience, as people worth talking and listening to – as respectable adults."

I do hope that this book can be viewed in a similar way. Nevertheless, it is reasonable to ask if the book is an example of voyeurism. If any reader considers it to be so then I recognise the implied reservation. However, it is not intended as such, but rather to inform those who have a natural curiosity concerning one of the strangest phenomena of nature to be found in our world.

Conjoined twins are often called 'Siamese twins' in reference to the famous Bunker twins found in Siam, i.e. present-day Thailand (see Chapter 2). The famous American showman P. T. Barnum probably coined this term. However, they were neither the first nor arguably the strangest example of this quirk of nature, and neither were they strictly Siamese, and so it is more correct to use the title 'conjoined twins'. It is also inappropriate to use the words 'freak' or 'mutant' or 'monster' or 'monstrocity', although they were much used in the past; today these terms have a derogatory flavour. 'Monster' was used for hundreds of years to include conjoined twins and, even as recently as 1993, Dudley Wilson's book *Signs and Portents* was subtitled *Monstrous Births from the Middle Ages to the Enlightenment*.

In 1903, a number of deformed individuals being exhibited in Barnum and Bailey's sideshow in the USA complained to their employer in these terms: "We the undersigned members of the Prodigy Department… were selected as a committee to draft a letter expressing our respectful though emphatic protest against the action of some person in your employ in placing in our hall a sign bearing the, to us, objectionable word freak and permitting another person to call aloud, 'This way to the freaks.'" Their protest was justified. It remains difficult to find a collective noun that refers to all individuals with physical or mental defects or anomalies unless it is 'physical or mental disability'. None of these words escape a taint of unseemliness or disrespect. In fact, the exhibits in Barnum and Bailey's circus were called 'curiosities'. However, 'conjoined twins' suffices for the subjects of this book.

For hundreds of years the phenomenon of conjoined twins, both in reality and in fiction, has provoked curiosity, horror, speculation, superstition and sheer wonder. Although rare, conjoined twins have been keenly observed and recorded in narrative and art. Such twins present a unique challenge to doctors, parents, society and, not least, to the twins themselves.

There follow descriptions of a number of human and animal examples of conjoined twins. In fact, hundreds have been described so this collection represents but a small selection. My choice of cases has been made to illustrate the various anatomical types and to describe the frequently remarkable circumstances of their births and the events of their lives. It is a strange coincidence that three famous sets of conjoined twins were buried in North Carolina: the Bunkers, McKoys and Hiltons.

From time to time conjoined twins hit the headlines when another couple are born and when surgeons attempt to separate them. There is also great interest and debate concerning the ethics of surgery, especially when in order to save one twin the life of the other must be sacrificed. There are many opinions about important issues. In the following chapters, big questions are addressed: How does this occur? Can it be prevented? What is the best management during pregnancy, birth and after birth? Further chapters deal with conjoined twins in mythology, fiction and entertainment and animals, also the psychology of twins is discussed.

Interest in conjoined twins does not wane. There have been many books (fiction and non-fiction), films, plays, songs, etc. Many examples can be found on the internet, including narratives, photos and videos. There have also been many artefacts, such as toys (see Chapter 15). The search term 'conjoined twins' produces more than 600,000 results on Google, although many are repeats. Some involve cartoons, even attempts at humour, and some are in bad taste. Viewing so many images can be disturbing. If you find it so just remind yourself of the extreme rarity of the condition, and stop surfing!

Just one example from the web should be mentioned, the Hensel twins (see Chapter 6), because their photos, videos and anatomical charts are so informative and of such good quality. One of their videos on YouTube entitled *The Twins Who Share a Body* is forty-five minutes long. They seem to welcome sensible media attention. Several other excellent videos and pictures are available under the website – *The Science of Conjoined Twins*. The BBC has shown several programmes which are available online. Of greatest interest is the *Horizon* programme broadcast on BBC2 on 19 October 2000. It is a discussion which included prominent surgeons and the Hensel and Krivoshlyapova twins. The actual programme is available on one site and the text on another. Go to 'BBC Horizon – Conjoined Twins' and look for the 19 October 2000 sites.

Support for conjoined twins and their families

For information, go to www.mayoclinic.org and then enter the term 'conjoined twins'.

The parents of the Ezell twins (see Chapter 7) run an international support group and are keen to give advice. See www.theezelltwins.weebly.com. Additional support groups may be found at Conjoined Twins Support Groups.

Nomenclature

Conjoined twins: twins physically joined together from before birth. Sometimes called Siamese twins but conjoined twins is the correct term. They are always of the same sex.

Monozygous (MZ): twins derived from one ovum and one sperm. Also sometimes called identical twins. However, though very similar, they are never absolutely identical. Their personalities may be very different. They are always of the same sex.

Dizygous (DZ): twins derived from two ova and two sperm. Also called fraternal twins. May be of the same or different sexes.

The eight main types of conjoined twins depend on which body parts are joined. The percentage frequencies of each type have been copied from Rowena Spencer's book *Conjoined Twins*, which reviewed 1000 cases.

> *Pagus:* a suffix meaning something fixed, from the French or Greek.
>
> *Parapagus:* the legs, pelvis and much of the abdomen are single. The upper body has varying degrees of unison. There may be one or two heads, and one or two thoraxes. Just over 25%
>
> *Thoracopagus:* joined at the chest, face to face, including heart. 17%
>
> *Omphalopagus:* joined more or less near the navel, as were the famous Bunker twins. Two separate hearts. 14%
>
> *Ischiopagus:* joined at the lower abdomen including external genitalia and anus, with four arms and legs. 12%
>
> *Cephalopagus:* joined face to face, from the skull to the umbilicus. 11%
>
> *Craniopagus:* joined at the skull. The brains may be joined, but the faces are not. About 5.5%
>
> *Pyopagus:* joined at the pelvis, may be back to back. There are usually four limbs. About 4%

Rachipagus: joined back to back from head to trunk with four limbs. Very rare.

Parasitic twin: a poorly formed twin without a functioning heart or brain joined to a virtually normal fetus. 3.9% (this figure obtained from paper by Mutchinick et al., see Bibliography)

Teratoma: not a true conjoined twin. This is a chaotic collection of twin tissue contained in an ovarian cyst which often contains hair and teeth. Also called a dermoid. The origin is unknown but there are several theories.

Fetus in fetu: fetal tissue enclosed within another fetus. Not true conjoined twins. Therefore likely to become a fetus within an adult.

Chapter 1

Early examples

Many images of conjoined twins in art have been discovered dating from several thousand years ago. These include rock art, sculptures and illustrations. Some may represent actual persons, others are products of the imagination. There are many actual examples as we advance into the Common Era.

Ain Ghazal

In 1974, thirty-two statues were found at a Neolithic site called Ain Ghazal, which is in Amman near Jordan. They are half human size and made of twigs covered in plaster. Three of them are two-headed (parapagus). They are thought to date from about 7000 BCE.

Anatolia

A marble goddess with two heads (parapagus) was found on the Anatolian plateau of Southern Turkey and thought to date from about 6500 BCE. James Mellaart excavated it between 1961 and 1963.

Giza, Egypt

In 1964, outside Cairo, a short drive from the Sphinx at Giza, a new-found tomb yielded no royal mummies or dazzling jewels. But the explorers were surprised to find on the wall, carved in stone, the images of two men embracing. Their names were inscribed as Niankhkhnum and Khnumhotep. Though not of the nobility, they were highly esteemed in the palace as the chief manicurists of the King sometime between 2380 BCE and 2320 BCE in the time known as the fifth dynasty of the Old Kingdom. Grooming the King was an honoured occupation. It was extremely rare in ancient Egypt for an elite tomb to be shared by two men of apparently equal standing. The usual practice was for such mortuary temples to be the resting place of one prominent man, together with his wife and children. It was most unusual for a couple of the same sex to be depicted locked in an embrace. In other scenes, they are also shown holding hands and nose-kissing, which was the favoured form of kissing in ancient Egypt. What do scholars make of their intimate relationship? It has been supposed that they were twins or gay, but David O'Connor, a New York Egyptologist, has stated, "My suggestion is that Niankhkhnum and Khnumhotep were indeed twins, but of a very special sort. They were conjoined twins [thoracopagus?]." However, most Egyptologists accept the normal-twins interpretation.

Tjatilco

Excavations at Tjatilco in Mexico, a village that was part of the Olmec district, which existed 3000 years ago, have found clay sculptures with a range of facial and cranial duplications. Tjatilco was famous for its pottery. Some of these sculptures are of small female figures, some with double faces (parapagus diprosopus) with a single shared eye together with two

2

normal eyes, while some have two heads. The faces and heads are developmentally and proportionately correct.

River Tigris
Some very early clay tablets of uncertain date were found near the River Tigris. They include an illustration of conjoined twins and were collected by King Ashurbanipal (668–627 BCE) who was an Assyrian king.

Moche, Lima, Peru
The Moche culture of ancient Peru has left numerous ceramics, dated about 300 BCE, famous for their erotic content, but also for an example of conjoined twins. They are now preserved in the Larco Museum in Lima.

Florence
There is a stone carving dated to 80 BCE which is now in the Museo St Marco in Florence. Other sculptures have been found in Australasia and Central America of uncertain age.

Anasazi
The Anasazi, thought to be the ancestors of Pueblo and/or Hopis Indians, left petroglyphs in New Mexico. The example shown was found in Colorado. The Anasazi occupied New Mexico from about 200 CE.

Cave drawings
There are cave drawings of conjoined twins. There are examples in south-western USA. There is one from Colorado City. Another is an example from Utah photographed by a friend of Ranger Kathryn in her blog and is thought to be 800 years old. See Ranger Kathryn's Arches.

Colorado plateau – Randy Langstraat
Rock art of a two-headed snake.

Roman coins
It has been claimed that images of conjoined twins occur on Roman coins, but the British Museum has not found any. Archaeologists have a habit of describing two heads which overlap, such as those of a king and queen, as conjoined.

St Augustine of Hippo
St Augustine, writing about 415 CE in his book *City of God*, described an example of a man having a double upper half with two heads and a single lower half (parapagus).

Abū al-Rayhān al-Bīrūnī
Al-Bīrūnī (973–1048 CE) described conjoined twins in his book *Kitab-al-Saidana*. He was a Persian Muslim scholar and polymath.

Byzantium (Constantinople)
Leo the Deacon, writing in his book *History*, provides a first-hand observation of seeing conjoined twins sometime during the mid-940s CE. "At this time male twins, who came from the region of Cappadocia, were wandering through many parts of the Roman Empire; I myself, who am writing these lines, have often seen them in Asia, a monstrous and novel wonder. For the various parts of their bodies were whole and complete, but their sides were attached from the armpit to the hip, uniting their bodies and combining them into one [rachipagus?]. And with the adjacent arms they embraced each other's necks, and in the others carried staffs, on which they supported themselves as they walked. They were thirty years old and well developed physically,

appearing youthful and vigorous. On long journeys they used to ride on a mule, sitting sideways on the saddle in the female fashion, and they had indescribably sweet and good dispositions."

Their chronicles from the tenth and eleventh centuries add more details. The boys were born in Armenia, but soon came to Constantinople during the reign of Romanus I Lecapenus (919–944 CE) where, in the words of Theophanes Continuatus, "they resided for a long time in the City and were admired by everybody as a curiosity but later were exiled because it was believed that they were a bad omen". Judging by Leo's remarks, the twins moved around the Byzantine Empire, perhaps in the same way as the travelling shows of the nineteenth and early twentieth centuries. The pair likely received similar reactions to those of the chroniclers – many would have seen them as a wonder or as a monster. However, the report by Leo also suggests that the two brothers were otherwise physically and mentally healthy. When one of the twins died, skilled doctors separated them cleverly at the line of connection with the hope of saving the surviving one but, after living three days, he also died. This is described in Chapter 11.

Polynesia
John Raffensperger, MD, reported finding artefacts of conjoined twins in various parts of Polynesia. At Easter Island, in a tourist shop, he found a woodcarving of two men joined at the waist and in the island's museum a two-headed Tahonga (a rare Aztec deity).

Mary and Eliza Chulkhurst, the Biddenden Maids

According to tradition, conjoined twin sisters were born in 1100 CE in the village of Biddenden in Kent, UK. Today, the villagers are clearly proud of the twins, hence the village sign, which was erected in 1922. The true facts have been difficult to discover. Antiquarians are divided as to the authenticity of the twins. Some think they may date from the sixteenth century. They reputedly lived for thirty-four years and were joined at the shoulders

Village sign in Biddenden village, Kent showing Chulkhurst twins.

and hips. However, an article in the *Gentleman's Magazine* of 1770 claims that the twins were joined from the waist down [pyopagus?]. The tradition also claims that, on the death of one twin, doctors intended to save the other but were deterred by the survivor, who declared, "As we came together, we will go together." The bodies were reputedly taken to the monks of Battle Abbey. However, no conjoined twins have ever been found to have two separate joins. The apparent join at the shoulders may represent the twins holding each other with their arms, so that the only join was at the hips.

No grave has been found, and neither has any will. Nevertheless, there are records showing that, for over 400 years, the income from twenty acres of land to the west of the church, believed to have been bequeathed by the twins, has been used for the poor. Today this is called the Chulkhurst Charity.

'Biscuit' showing Chulkhurst twins, sold at Biddenden every Easter.

Traditionally, the charity provided bread, cheese and beer to the needy at Easter time. The distribution took place inside the church and was accompanied by much disorder. One report states that the distribution was cancelled in 1605 when the Archdeacon of Canterbury attended. In 1645, and again in 1656, the rector tried unsuccessfully to claim the charity money for the church rather than the village. In 1682, the rector, Giles Hinton, reported to the archbishop, "Which custom even to this time is with much disorder and indecency". After this the dole took place in the church porch until the end of the nineteenth century, when it was transferred to the workhouse (poorhouse). It takes place to this day on Easter Monday, though the building is no longer a workhouse. Today the dole takes the form of biscuits made of flour and water. They are hard and are not meant to be eaten. There was a time when they were thought to be a cure for stomach ache. The clothing depicted on the biscuit is somewhat sixteenth century, which is when records of the charity began. It has been suggested that the maids on the biscuits represent recipients of the charity and that their image mistakenly gave rise to the idea of conjoined twins.

Today the distribution is peaceful, as I can testify having visited in 2001 and purchased some of the biscuits. The current biscuit is slightly different to any of the three illustrated in Jan Bondeson's book *The Two-Headed Boy*, so they must have been redesigned several times over the years, though retaining a similar image of the twins and the same dates. They are certainly acceptable souvenirs of what remains a fascinating historic tradition, the creditability of which may never be confirmed.

A poem found in the documents of the Chulkhurst Charity testifies to a stained-glass image of the twins in the parish church, which has since disappeared:

> *The moon on the east oriel shone*
> *Through slender shafts of shapely stone*
> *The silver light so pale and faint*
> *Shewed the twin sisters and many a saint*
> *Whose images on the glass were dyed:*
> *Mysterious maidens side by side.*
> *The moon beam kissed the holy pane,*
> *and threw on the pavement a mystic stain*

In 1907, the Chulkhurst Charity was merged with other local charities to provide for the needy at Easter and to give money at Christmas time. The original twenty acres were sold and have been built on.

Rutland Psalter

This Psalter was made about 1260. It features many fantastic marginal images including an example of conjoined twins.

Rutland Psalter 1260, decorated with conjoined twins. British Library Board Ms 629251.72.

Plague twins

In 1349, the plague known as The Black Death was spreading rapidly northward through England. The birth of conjoined twins in Kingston upon Hull in Yorkshire frightened the superstitious people, who regarded this as a bad omen. The twins lived only a few days. The plague did indeed arrive in Yorkshire that very year.

The Scottish brothers

These boys were born near Glasgow in the fifteenth century and lived for twenty-eight years. They were double above the waist and single below (parapagus). King James IV of Scotland saw them and arranged for their care and education. They learned to sing and play instruments and were also reputed to be able to speak about eight languages. They died in 1518.

The girls of Worms, Germany

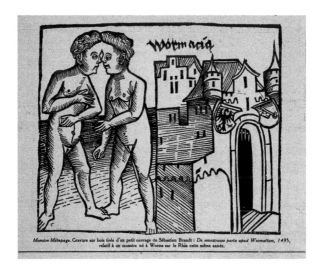

Twins born 1495. Woodcut by Sebastien Brandt,
Worms on Rhine, Germany.
Welcome Library, Licence CC BY.

These girls were born in 1495 with their foreheads joined (craniopagus). An explanation was recorded by Sebastian Munster in 1552 as follows: "As the mother of these two children was gossiping with another woman upon the street an unexpected thing happened and struck the foreheads of the two women together. There-upon the pregnant woman became ill with fright, so that the fruit within her womb had to suffer for it." *Quoted by Spencer, 2003*

The Siamese twins of Spain

These twins are notable as being the first to be recorded as having been subjected to a post-mortem examination. This occurred in 1533 in Santo Domingo at the request of a priest, who had pondered whether the twins had one soul or two. He had performed two baptisms and wondered if he had made a mistake. The autopsy was conducted in accordance with the procedure of the time, namely two doctors supervising a surgeon. They found two hearts so were able to reassure the parents that they were two "when they passed from this life to celestial glory". The priest was greatly relieved that the twins must have had two souls, thus justifying the double baptism. This must have been the first and only post-mortem ever performed to study the soul of the deceased!

Sixteenth-century broadsheets

Such broadsheets (leaflets) were a common method of news distribution. In Elizabethan times (sixteenth century), broadsheets containing news or stories in verse were frequently sold for a halfpenny or one penny each and often sung by the seller, hence being called ballads. These single sheets were the main source of news. Seventeen of 3081 examples registered with the Stationer's Company of London record birth defects, of which nearly half describe conjoined twins. They were often regarded as signs of God's wrath and as important heralds of misfortune. A negative understanding of these births has consequently dominated studies of the phenomenon. Yet a number of pre-Reformation publications represent such births, both textually and visually, in positive terms. Children perceived as monstrous could be viewed in a sympathetic light, interpreted as positive political omens and even represented in the guise of the infant Christ.

16th century broadsheet, London.

Lazarus and Joannes Colloredo

These twins were born in 1617 in Genoa, Italy. They were one complete individual, with an attached incomplete twin having a head and two arms, known as a parasitic twin. An anatomist called Bartholinus studied them in detail. Joannes, the parasite, had a head and two arms. They were exhibited all over Europe. In 1642, they met King Charles I in London. They toured Europe in 1646 but there is no record of what happened after that.

Bartholinus reported that Lazarus married and had several normal children. There is a story that Lazarus killed a man and was sentenced to death but reprieved because execution would kill the innocent parasite!

A broadsheet in 1637 included this poem:

The imperfect one the small poxe had,
Which made the perfect brother sad,
But he had never any,
And if you nip it by the arme,
(This hath been tride by many,)
It like an infant (with voice weake)
Will cry out though it cannot speake

Two more poems:

Yet nothing doth the lesser eate,
He's onely nourish'd with the meate
Wherewith the other feeds,
By which it seems though outward parts
They have for two, yet not two hearts.
This admiration breeds.

A Gentleman well qualifide,
Doth beare his brother at his side,
inseparably knit
As in this figure you may see,
And both together living be
The world admires at it.

The Fair Maids of Foscott
The famous diarist Samuel Pepys (1633–1703) recorded a visit made on 12 June 1668 to the village church of Norton St Philip, a hamlet in Somerset, England. "I walked to the church… and here saw the tombstone whereon there were only two heads cut, which, the story goes, and credibly, were two sisters, called the Fair Maids of Foscott, that had two bodies upwards and one belly, and there lie buried [parapagus]." When Pepys saw the tomb, the effigy of the two sisters was cut in stone on the floor of the nave. This

has since disappeared except for the two heads that are set on the wall inside the tower. Almost nothing is known about these twins. Their dates are unknown but likely to be well before 1668.

Fair Maids of Foscott. Image in church of Norton St Philip, Somerset with Samuel Pepys's quote, 1668.

Twins buried in a box

Sometime in the seventeenth century, James Paris du Plessis, while digging in his family garden in Pluviers, France, found a buried box containing a two-headed conjoined-twin male baby; presumably it had been stillborn. James was aged fifteen at the time and was a servant to Samuel Pepys. Apparently his mother had allowed a Madame Souville to deliver her child in their house. During her pregnancy, against her husband's wishes, she is alleged to have studied a French book containing a picture of two-headed conjoined twins, and this was thought to be the cause of the deformity. The dead baby was secretly buried in the garden. Subsequently, du Plessis wrote about this incident in his book *Prodigies and Monstrous Births*.

Elizabeth and Catherine

The first successful separation occurred at Basle, Switzerland in 1689. This incident is described in Chapter 11.

Hungarian sisters of Szony

Helen and Judith were born in 1701 in Szony, Hungary. Their conjoined state was attributed to "the force of the mother's imagination during the period of gestation". They shared an anus but had separate vaginas (pyopagus).

Hélène and Judith. Known as the Hungarian Sisters, born 1701 in Szony, Hungary. Welcome Library licence CC BY/4.0.

From the ages of two to nine years, the sisters were exhibited in Holland, Germany, England, France, Italy and Poland. They became talented singers and spoke Hungarian, High Dutch, German, French and some English. During the seventh year of their exhibition career, all the top scientists of Europe examined them, and all aspects of their bodies and personalities were described in great detail. At the age of nine they were placed in the convent of the nuns of St Ursula in Presburg, Hungary, where they remained for the rest of their lives. From the age of sixteen they menstruated approximately a week apart from each other. In 1723, Helen died suddenly, quickly followed by Judith.

A poem by Alexander Pope, translated from the Latin, is inscribed on their tomb:

> *Two sisters wonderful to behold, who have thus grown as one,*
> *That naught their bodies can divide, no power beneath the sun.*

14

The town of Szony gave them birth, hard by far-famed
Komorn,
Which noble fort may all the arts of Turkish sultans scorn.
Lucina, woman's gentle friend, did Helen first receive;
And Judith, when three hours had passed, her mother's
womb did leave.
One urine passage serves for both; one anus, so they tell;
The other parts their numbers keep, and serve their
owners well.
Their parents' poor did send them forth, the world to
travel through,
That this great wonder of the age should not be hid from
view.
The inner parts concealed do lie hid from our eyes, alas!
But all the body here you view erect in solid brass.

John Hunter's case

The double skull of a child (craniopagus) was given to the famous London surgeon John Hunter (1728–1793). It now resides in the museum of the Royal College of Surgeons in London. The boys were born in Calcutta in 1783. Apparently, after birth the horrified midwife threw them into a fire. However, they survived and were then exhibited for money by their mother. They died of a cobra bite at about four years of age. The body was later

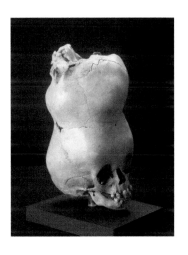

The double skull of a child given to the famous London surgeon John Hunter (1728–1793) is in the museum of the Royal College of Surgeons, London.

dug up by the East India Company's agent and brought to England. The head of the first boy is not malformed; the other head is deformed, the ears and teeth are absent, the eyes are present but one had been injured by the fire. The brains are separate.

Chapter 2

Chang and Eng Bunker
– nineteenth century

Early life

The most famous example of conjoined twins, Chang and Eng Bunker (the so-called 'original Siamese twins'), were born on 11 May 1811 in a village on the Meklong river, sixty miles west of Bangkok in Siam (present-day Thailand). Their fame resulted in the words 'Siamese twins' being added to dictionaries. They had a Chinese father and a Chinese/Siamese mother; therefore they were a quarter Siamese and three-quarters Chinese. Years later their mother informed an American that she had suffered no greater inconvenience at their birth than with her other children and that they were born with the head of one between the legs of the other. There was a band of tissue joining their bodies at the lower parts of their chests. It must have been quite flexible. They were the first-born of their parents, who are reputed to have gone on to produce four more sets of twins, none of them conjoined, and four single births.

At first, the joining ligament restricted their posture but as they grew it stretched so that they became able to stand side by side. Chang is the one on the left when they stand facing. When they were young, Siamese people thought the twins to be a dangerous omen so doctors advised dividing them, while King Rama II wanted them killed. Their mother stoutly resisted these suggestions, so their lives were saved.

From a poem by Edward Bulwer-Lytton (written in 1831 when the twins were twenty years old):

The Bunker twins. Welcome Library. Licence: CC BY 4.0.

> *A single voice appals the ear,*
> *And tells – but with a whispered breath –*
> *"How easy is an infant's death.*
> *"And that we only do fulfil laws*
> *"Given by Nature – to deny*
> *"Life to the wretched things that mock*
> *"Nature herself! –*
>
> *The gossip ceased; and you might mark*
> *The influence of her words creeping*
> *And in the pause, and thro' the dark,*
> *You heard the mother's quiet weeping.*

And wild and thrilling though the crowd,
And thus, our Twins were saved to flow
Thro' Time's stream in rhyme and glory,
The heroes of an English story.

They grew up in a floating house, their father being a fisherman. They became good swimmers. Chang grew up to be the quick-tempered dominant twin, while Eng was more docile. They were very devoted to their mother throughout their lives in spite of prolonged separation from her.

When they were aged six, smallpox struck, killing one brother and two sisters. The twins survived, suffering only mild attacks. In 1819 there was a cholera epidemic in Siam which resulted in the death of the twins' father and five of their nine siblings. The eight-year-old twins survived but the family were destitute. They managed to earn money by fishing and later by market trading, particularly with preserved ducks' eggs. They mostly agreed with each other, Eng usually giving in to Chang if there was a disagreement. However, they had a fight which caused their mother to intervene.

One day they were accused with other suspects of stealing valuable peacock feathers. A court imposed a trial by ordeal. All the suspects had to swallow an emetic, and whoever vomited would be considered guilty. The twins kept the emetic down while an innocent man vomited and was punished. Later, the true culprit was found.

In 1824, a Scottish trader called Robert Hunter arrived in Siam. While wandering around Meklong he came upon the twins swimming near their home. He soon made friends with their family and conceived the idea of taking the twins to the West, where they could be exhibited for money.

At the age of fourteen the twins were summoned to Bangkok to meet King Rama III. The meeting was accompanied by most elaborate ceremonial rituals. The King asked many questions, after which the twins were given a tour of the various temples. Finally, they were given many presents from the King and several of his wives. Soon after this, Hunter asked the King if he could take the twins to the West. The King refused because he wanted to send the twins with a mission to Cochin China. In Saigon they witnessed a cruel fight between a tiger and many elephants.

Some years later another trader arrived, Captain Abel Coffin, an American, who brought firearms from Calcutta for the King. Coffin was a good friend of the King so Hunter enlisted his help in persuading the King to allow the twins to leave. The twins and the King were agreeable, though their mother was reluctant until she was paid a considerable sum and was promised that the twins would return after two and a half years, when they would be aged twenty-one. They never did return.

To the West
Hunter and Coffin agreed that they would share equally the profit to be made from exhibiting the twins. In the nineteenth century, a great deal of money was made by freak shows though, by the twentieth century, these fortunes had declined due to increasing public disapproval.

On 1 April 1829, the twins, aged nearly eighteen, departed from Bangkok with Hunter and Coffin, a pet python and a boy friend named Teiu. During the journey, Hunter left the ship and proceeded to England. The twins enjoyed the voyage, spending time climbing the masts and playing with the crew. They became so good at draughts (chequers) that no one could beat them, not even the crew member who had taught them. Their only regret was that the python escaped and was lost overboard. They arrived at Boston, Massachusetts on 16 August 1829.

After admiring the city, so different from the villages of Siam, the twins were examined by doctors. The most detailed examination was performed by Dr John Collins Warren, Professor of Anatomy and Surgery at Harvard. He noted that the connecting band was 2 inches long at its upper edge and 5 inches at its lower edge. He observed one umbilicus near one end of the band. He thought that the band was composed of cartilage, and possibly a continuation of the peritoneal cavity. He considered that surgical separation would be dangerous and should only be attempted if one of the twins died. At that time, opening the peritoneal cavity was rightly considered to be dangerous due to the risk of infection. It seems that the twins did not want to be separated, and of course Hunter and Coffin did not desire it. Finally, Dr Warren predicted that the twins would only live for a few years. Coffin enlisted James Webster Hale to look after the twins and to be their business agent. Eng was 5 feet 3.5 inches tall but Chang was an inch shorter and so had special shoes made to compensate for the difference.

Two weeks after arrival in Boston, the twins were exhibited in a huge tent to vast crowds, billed as 'The Siamese Double Boys'. Later the exhibition moved to the Exchange Coffee House. Newspapers reported debates: what if one twin became Christian while the other remained Buddhist, would one be saved or both lost? What if one committed a crime: could both be jailed or neither?

> *For well we know if one by chance*
> *To Fleet or Bench is sent.*
> *The other would an action bring*
> *For false imprisonment.*
>
> *Edward Bulwer-Lytton*

(*Fleet*: famous former London prison. *Bench*: magistrate.)

This last dilemma actually occurred years later and has also been exploited by fiction writers. The twins developed their act by adding somersaults and backflips, and challenged the audience to games of draughts. They toured to Providence, Rhode Island, New York and Philadelphia.

To Britain

On 17 October 1829 they set sail for England with Coffin, Coffin's wife, Hale and Teiu. Coffin took out a life insurance policy on the twins and gave instructions that, in the event of their death, they should be conveyed to the ship's destination, for he realised that even their dead bodies would be valuable. They later discovered that Coffin had booked them in steerage, even though he told them he had booked them in first class, blaming the Captain for the error. They docked at Southampton on 8 November 1829 and proceeded overland to London. They took rooms at the North and South American Coffee House. They

Bunkers fraternising in London. Fanciful illustration from E G Bulwer's poem 'The Siamese Twins' 1831. Drawn and etched by W H Brooke.

were to spend fourteen months in the British Isles. They met members of the Royal Family but probably did not meet King George IV as he was ill. On 26 June 1830 the King died, to be succeeded by King William IV. Hunter arranged a big meeting of the twins with several doctors, other distinguished persons and newspaper reporters.

A Dr George Buckley Bolton was appointed their personal physician. Dr Peter Mark Roget, secretary of the Royal Society and who is famous as the author of *Roget's Thesaurus*, still used today, examined them. During this time the twins learnt English. The boy Teiu was sent back to Siam as he didn't get on with the others. A beautiful young woman called Sophia is reputed to have fallen in love with both twins. She wrote:

> *How happy could I be with either,*
> *Were the other dear charmer away.*

She was ready to marry both but, when told this would be bigamy, a crime, she abandoned the idea. They were exhibited to big crowds from December 1830. The advertising blurb included the words, "In their figure, countenance, manners and movements, there is nothing that can offend the delicacies of the most fastidious female." They were seen by Queen Adelaide, the wife of William IV, the Duke of Wellington and many other notable people. After several months in London they made an extensive tour of England, Scotland and Ireland.

Coffin wished to show the twins in France but was refused permission. The French officials stated that maternal fantasies could be harmful to pregnant women as they could deform their unborn children and deprave the minds of their children. This was a popular superstition but did not bother the people of the USA and Britain. They visited many other parts of continental Europe with great success.

Bunkers arrested in London. Fanciful illustration from E G Bulwer's poem 'The Siamese Twins' 1831. Drawn and etched by W H Brooke.

The possibility of surgical separation must have been considered. One point of view about this was offered in the *Literary Gazette*:

> *If in the page of Holy Writ we find*
> *That man should not divide what God hath joined,*
> *O why, with nicest skill, should science dare*
> *To separate this Heaven-united pair?*
> *United by a more than legal band,*
> *A wonder wrought by the Creator's hand!*

Return to America

The twins left Portsmouth on 12 January 1831 and arrived in New York on 4 March. Robert Hunter had sold his interest in the twins to Captain Coffin, who had returned to trade in the Far East. Coffin's wife, Susan, and his assistant, Captain William Davis, Jr., would now look after the twins, together with James Hale as business manager. Many people wrongly assumed that the twins' mother had sold them to Hunter.

They were aged nineteen as they began their American tour in New York. They were to tour the USA for most of the next eight years, visiting fourteen of the twenty states, and they also went to Canada and Cuba. During this time it could be said that they matured from Siamese boys to American men.

In 1830, Senator Daniel Webster declaimed for political union, saying, "The sentiment dear to every true American heart – Liberty and Union, now and forever, one and inseparable." This became a popular slogan, printed in schoolbooks, and was used in publicity for the Bunker twins. Actually, it was somewhat ironic as the twins supported the Confederates in the Civil War!

The touring lifestyle became a strain, causing the twins to become unhappy and less tolerant of the public. During a show in Athens, Alabama, a doctor from the audience accused them of being a fraud and tried to convince the audience. Understandably, this angered the twins, who promptly punched the doctor to the floor. This resulted in a full-scale riot, with some people siding with the twins and some with the doctor, until the police arrived. The twins were arrested and fined $350.

In Philadelphia, a spectator shook hands with Chang but squeezed his hand painfully. Chang punched him. The twins were arrested. A judge pronounced that Chang should go to prison but that this would be false arrest for Eng so that the complainant could be prosecuted. As a result, the charge was dropped.

A fanciful poem by Edward Bulwer-Lytton:

> "I [Eng] made the row, sir, I alone,
> While Chang was gazing on the sky, sir;
> He prest me greatly to come on,
> But such a girl was in my eye, sir!
> And so, not deeming it could hurt
> You or your laws, I stopped to flirt;
> And tho' my weakness you may blame, sir,
> Perhaps you might have done the same, sir."

> "But one word more: in this affair,
> If I have sinned, my sin not knowing,
> As you may deem it worth bestowing;
> But he – my brother – no offence
> Committed; you must let him hence!
> Take me to prison, if you please,
> And while to jail the guilty sending,
> Take heed, not touch the unoffending!"

At Lynnfield, Massachusetts, the twins were shooting in some woods when a crowd accosted them. An argument developed, during which one of the twins struck a man and they fired their guns, which contained only powder. They were arrested. The judge fined them and bound them over to keep the peace.

In 1831, Hale fell out with Mrs Coffin, accusing her of being insulting to his wife. He resigned and was replaced by an Irish friend of Hale called Charles Harris. The twins would be twenty-one years of age on 11 May 1832. As this date approached they wished to speak personally to either Captain or Mrs Coffin but were unable to do so as the Captain was at sea returning from the Far East. However, on their birthday they announced that they were now free of their contract, conveying this decision to Mrs Coffin by letter. She disputed their right to do this but they insisted that the Captain had promised freedom on their twenty-first birthday. The twins took their freedom, believing that the Captain had swindled them of much of the money they had earnt, though this is unlikely to be true. However, he did fail to pay the $500 he owed to the twins' mother. The twins continued touring with Charles Harris, whom they had employed as their manager. On Coffin's return to America he pursued the twins, met them but failed to regain control of them.

In 1833, a Kentucky woman gave birth to stillborn conjoined twins. She blamed this on having seen several illustrations of the Bunker twins. 1835 was a very busy year for the twins. It included more touring in the USA, a tour of Cuba, a visit to Canada and then a voyage to France, which had reversed its previous refusal to allow them entry. They enjoyed Paris, were exhibited and examined by doctors. One of them speculated that the joining of the twins had occurred during the end of the first month of the pregnancy.

Also in 1836 a tour was undertaken to Belgium and Holland, and they then returned to the USA. There was more touring, including exhibitions in museums. They met Dr James Calloway, who became a lifelong friend; he invited them to holiday at Wilkesboro, North Carolina. This was to be a significant move in their lives.

To North Carolina

In North Carolina, a beautiful but backward state compared to its neighbours, it was hard work on the farms for the slaves, while the wealthier white folk enjoyed hunting, fishing and spirit-distilling. The twins liked the place and the people. They were soon able to indulge their desire for hunting deer and foxes, and fishing for trout and perch. It was a relief to leave behind the constant touring. Not long before, they had been thinking about returning to Siam but this desire faded as they were falling in love with this congenial environment. Although the twins had made a lot of money they needed to earn a living. They opened a general store but it failed. They turned to farming, bought 150 acres for $300 and later bought another sixty-four acres at Traphill, Wilkes County, North Carolina, near the Blue Ridge Mountains. They built a two-storey house, other buildings for slaves and a stable. Furniture was bought in New York or made locally.

They needed slaves to run their farm; that was the system. However, it was not the system for non-whites to own slaves. The twins' ownership complicated people's understanding of slave-holding as a white institution. Their marriages will shortly be described. Their increasing number of mixed-race children forced Americans to confront this phenomenon. What did the twins think about slavery? They supported the Confederacy in the Civil War, but we don't know if they had any doubts about its justification. Was the Civil War more to do with politics than slavery? They seem to have accepted slavery and also its eventual abolition without much difficulty, even though this caused financial loss.

In 1839 they decided to become citizens of North Carolina and America. However, on applying to the Naturalisation Office they were told they would need to have first names and a surname. Up to this time the twins had never had a surname. According to Wallace's biography, in 1840 they decided on the name Bunker after the name of friends they had made in New York years before. According to Kay Hunter's book, a bystander suggested the name when they were asked their surname. It is surprising that they were allowed to become citizens as federal law only allowed this for white persons.

Charles Harris, who had continued to accompany the twins, married Fannie Bauguess. The twins attended the wedding, where they met two young women: eighteen-year-old Sarah Yates, usually called Sallie, and her seventeen-year-old sister, Adelaide. They were the daughters of wealthy farmer David Yates and his wife Nancy. Nancy was exceptionally obese, too heavy for any scales that were available.

Soon the twins were making frequent visits to the Yates household, where they were welcomed. They fell in love with the daughters but for a long time did not know if their feelings were reciprocated. The twins developed their farm with corn crops, cows and pigs. Dr Calloway became their family doctor. The twins continued a close friendship with the Harris family, who lived nearby. They felt anxiety and diffidence about the practicality of marriage to the sisters. They confided in Harris, who shared their concerns. However, eventually they managed to declare their love and the sisters accepted the prospect of marriage.

Before telling the sisters' parents they appeared publicly as a foursome in Wilkesboro. People were shocked. According to Kay Hunter, a descendant of Robert Hunter, a crowd attacked the Yates' house and threatened to burn his crops if David allowed the match. However, the biography by Joseph Orser casts doubts as to whether there was such violence as nothing about this appeared in contemporary newspapers or letters. He also suggests that the Wallace biography copied the errors from Hunter's book.

David and Nancy Yates were shocked and commanded their daughters to leave the twins. It is thought that the parents' objection was not to the twins' conjoined state but to their race and nationality. The twins appealed to Pastor Colby Sparks to intercede. He was sympathetic and tried to persuade the Yates but failed. They then asked Methodist minister James Davis for help but he also failed to move the implacable Yates. The sisters were now virtual prisoners in their own house. While the twins brooded on their sad fate they received a note from the sisters suggesting a secret tryst. So they met secretly several times until they all decided to get married without the parents' approval.

At this point the twins thought that their conjoined state would indeed be a significant problem, so they seriously considered surgical separation. They consulted the College of Surgeons at Philadelphia, being fully aware of the risks, and persuaded the surgeons to operate. They returned to Philadelphia at the appointed time but, the day before the operation, the sisters turned up to dissuade them. After a long discussion, the twins finally agreed not to have surgery.

The parents still objected. In desperation, the lovers planned to elope and get married by Colby Sparks, the Baptist minister. Before they could do this the parents relented and agreed to the marriages. Licences were obtained from Wilkes County. Three days later, on 13 April 1843, the marriages were performed by Reverend James Davis, the Methodist minister, in the presence of a small group of friends. Chang married Adelaide, who was aged nineteen, and Eng married Sarah, who was aged twenty. The twins were aged thirty-two years. The ceremonies were followed by a feast and dancing, after which the couples retired to Trap House, where a specially made wide bed awaited them. The marriages were to last until the twins died, nearly thirty-one years later. As the Wallace biography declared, "Love Conquers All".

The brides became pregnant within about four weeks of the marriages. Sarah's first child was a girl called Katherine Marcellus, while Adelaide's first was a daughter called Josephine Virginia, born just six days after Katherine. These were the first of many children. People asked, "How do they do it?" Well, clearly they adapted to the situation but exactly how we shall never know. Probably the twins developed the ability for one of them to 'blank out', i.e. to be oblivious to his brother's activity. In fact, to 'turn off' while the other 'turned on'. In the twentieth century, the Hilton conjoined twins reported their ability to do this, having been taught by Houdini. Was this a sort of self-hypnosis?

Bunker's chair, double seat. Reputedly found at American Antique Fair.

They acquired two new doctors, brothers Joseph and William Hollingsworth, who became lifelong friends. They grew tobacco, which their slaves made into chewing tobacco. The twins were fond of tobacco, cigars, pipes and chewing. They grew wheat, rye, oats, peas, beans, potatoes and fruit, and kept cows, sheep, pigs, fowl and bees. They instituted the latest farming methods and machinery to such an extent that neighbouring farmers came to inspect and learn. They were skilled carpenters and were thought to have invented the 'double-chop technique', whatever that may be. They helped build White Plains Baptist Church and installed a two-seater pew for themselves. This shows some interest in the Church. Their actual beliefs are unknown; perhaps they developed a syncretism of Buddhist and Christian beliefs. Certainly their wives were keen Christians.

In politics they supported the South and the Whig party. By 1860 the twins owned twenty-eight slaves. David Yates, the father-in-law of the twins, had given them a slave called Grace Gates as a wedding present. She was known as Aunt Grace. She looked after the children of both twins, became a respected friend and was retained as a paid servant when slavery was abolished. She appears in the photo on page. 42 of this MS. She is reputed to have outlived them all.

The twins' interests included hunting, shooting, fishing, music (both played the flute), poetry, especially the works of Alexander Pope and Shakespeare, draughts, chess and poker. They were skilled at breaking in horses. There were times when the twins quarrelled, even on at least one occasion indulging in a fist fight. This was reported to a magistrate, who fined them a nominal fee. They fell out over whisky as Chang drank excessively while Eng was a moderate drinker.

An argument occurred between the twins and two men, Colonel Gerry and Mr Prescott. The Colonel accused them of being liars. This provoked one of the twins to strike with the butt of his gun. The Colonel threw a stone that hit one of the twins' heads, causing bleeding. One twin fired his gun but it was only loaded with powder. The police arrived. In court the twins had to pay a $200 bond guaranteeing their good behaviour. After another violent fracas the twins had to pay a $350 bond.

The twins had maintained contact with Robert Hunter, who had continued to trade with Siam. However, he quarrelled with the authorities and was expelled from Siam. He died years later in his native Scotland. A year later their friend Charles Harris died. Both deaths greatly distressed the twins. The Bunker families continued to grow: eventually Eng and Sarah had six boys and five girls, while Chang and Adelaide had three boys and seven girls, two of whom were deaf mutes, making a grand total of twenty-one children.

Back to show business
A larger family meant larger expenses so, after ten years in retirement from show business, the twins decided to return. In 1849 they exhibited in New York but this was unsuccessful

as there was competition from the famous Tom Thumb, who was being shown at that time.

Back home, the twins found their house getting too crowded, which caused bad feeling between the families. Therefore, in 1852, the Bunkers bought another house in Mount Airy for Adelaide and some of her children, while Sallie remained at the farm. The twins divided their time between the two residences.

Eng and Sallie's house.

Chang and Adelaide's house.

They tried touring again in 1853, accompanied by one of Chang's sons and one of Eng's daughters. The tour lasted one year, beginning in Boston; they travelled 4700 miles, visiting 130 towns in the USA and Canada.

In 1857 they decided to have a separate house and farm for each family. Dividing their wealth equally was tricky but was achieved with the help of independent advisers. Eng kept the original house while Chang had a new house built a mile away. Each twin spent three days at one house and then three at the other.

In 1860 they went to New York again, this time appearing at Barnum's American Museum, where the Prince of Wales, the future King Edward VII, visited them. They did not like Barnum and he did not like them. They refused an offer to tour in Barnum's circus.

They then chose California, where the population had been rising rapidly during the previous ten years because of the gold

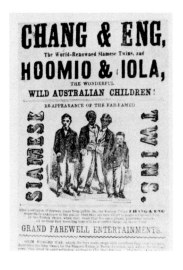

Advertisement in New York 1866.

rush. They also chose California because from there they would be able to make a sentimental journey back across the Pacific to Siam, which they had left thirty-one years before. In 1849 they had received letters from a Christian missionary in Siam and from their brother telling them of their mother's death. Their father and stepfather had also died. The letter from the brother said, "The mother of Mr In and Mr Chun died on the year of the goat, first month, 6th day of full moon [28 December 1847]".

They travelled with their two children by ship to the Isthmus of Panama, across which a railway had recently been built, and then by ship to San Francisco. At that time there was anti-Chinese sentiment in San Francisco as a result of the immigration of many Chinese. The twins abandoned their plan to visit Siam when they heard of the danger of civil war. They appeared in San Francisco, Sacramento and other cities, staying only two months before starting their journey home. While on their way to California, Southern Carolina seceded from the Union followed by other Southern states to form the Confederate States of America.

Civil War

The twins and their two sons returned home in March 1861, a month before the Civil War began. At that time, Eng had sixteen slaves and Chang had twelve. Eng's wife, together with their neighbour, organised a school for their children and the slaves. Opinion in North Carolina was divided although most, including the twins, supported the South. In May, North Carolina joined the Confederation. The state contributed 111,000 troops to the South, of whom over 40,000 died. Chang's eldest son, Christopher, served in the Confederate army, was injured, captured and released in a prisoner exchange scheme. One of Eng's sons also served and was wounded. Towards the end of the war Union troops, led by Major General Stoneman, occupied Mount Airy. The General tried to force local men chosen by ballot to join his army. Eng's name came up but not Chang's! Eng was let off. When the South was defeated the twins lost a lot of money as the Southern currency collapsed and, at a stroke, they lost their thirty-three slaves. The slaves marched off in triumph but many returned to be employed by the twins. Aunt Grace remained with the Bunkers.

To Europe

Short of money, the twins decided to tour again and so in 1865, at the age of fifty-four, they began in Chicago. In 1866 they toured with conjoined twins Millie and Christine McKoy (see Chapter 3). By 1868 they were rich again. In that year they departed for another tour, this time of Great Britain, managed by Barnum. (At this time the twins considered again if it might be possible to be separated, perhaps by surgeons in Britain.) They took with them Eng's oldest daughter, Katherine, who suffered some kind of chronic illness, thinking that they may get help from physicians in London or Edinburgh. They also took Chang's daughter Nannie. On the way to New York they visited Chang's two deaf mute children who attended the Institute for Deaf and Dumb and Blind in Raleigh, North Carolina. They also visited President Johnson in Washington.

They arrived in Liverpool and took a train to Edinburgh, where their show began. Doctors who saw Katherine diagnosed 'pulmonary consumption', which they said was incurable. It is possible that she had pulmonary tuberculosis. The family had expected bad news.

The twins consulted Sir James Young Simpson, famous as the first person to demonstrate the anaesthetic quality of chloroform. He had also invented a new kind of obstetric forceps. Simpson later wrote, "The operation is certainly possible, and would be attended probably with little, or indeed no difficulty; but it would be so perilous in its character that the twins could not in my opinion be justified in submitting to it... The cutaneous, cartilaginous, vascular and other tissues composing the walls and mass of the band offer in themselves no special obstruction to its surgical division. The interior of the band, however, contains, I believe, a canal or diverticulum of peritoneum that passes from the abdominal cavity of one brother to the abdominal cavity of the other. Still the danger of cutting through a diverticulum of peritoneum is too great to ever be done without grave and urgent reasons; and none such exist in this case." [This is no problem today.] They then consulted a Professor Sogine regarding possible surgery; his opinion was the same.

Several other surgeons in various countries also opposed surgery, except those consulted just before their marriages. In fact, when an autopsy was eventually performed, the diverticula of peritoneum from each twin were found not to communicate. Therefore it may be conjectured that the surgeons could have kept the two peritoneal cavities apart, but they would have had to divide the bridge of liver.

In 1869, the twins took an extensive tour of Scotland and England. They had an audience with Queen Victoria, who was very concerned to know if separation would be possible. She consulted her physician, Sir William Jenner, about it. In a letter of 1 January 1869 to her daughter, the Crown Princess of Prussia, the Queen stated that a Dr Nelaton in Paris was to attempt surgery. This did not materialise, as they did not visit France on this European trip. In another letter of 31 March to the Princess, the Queen enclosed a photo of the twins which she described as "very horrid". However, she gave each of them a gold watch and chain. The twins then took a short tour of Ireland before returning to the USA.

Advertisement in London 1869.
British Library Board. EVAN 482.

After just five months in the USA the twins embarked on the most ambitious tour of their lives. In 1870, aged fifty-nine, they sailed from New York with two of their sons to Hamburg and then to Berlin. They visited Dr Rudolf Virchow, a famous doctor and also an eminent scientist, especially in the field of pathology. The twins hoped he would approve surgery. He did not. They travelled to St Petersburg and then to Moscow, where they met Czar Alexander II. They performed in many Russian cities and had hoped to proceed to Austria, Italy and Spain. However, the Franco-Prussian war intervened, compelling them to return to the USA. During the voyage home, Chang suffered a stroke that paralysed his right arm and leg.

Last years

Dr Hollingsworth's grandson made the following report: Dr Joseph Hollingsworth prescribed applications of cold water which Chang objected to. After a while he was able to walk with a crutch. Chang increased his alcohol intake which served as another kind of crutch, frequently getting drunk. This resulted in quarrels with Eng. During one exceptionally heated quarrel they went to the doctor and demanded immediate surgical separation. Dr Hollingsworth prepared his knives and is reputed to have said, "Very well, just get on the table and I'll fix you, but which would you prefer, that I should sever the flesh that connects you or cut off your heads? One will produce just about the same results as the other." That brought them to their senses; they calmed down and shook hands. Other reports stated that the twins got on very well at this time.

On 12 January 1874, Chang complained of a cough and chest pains. Dr Hollingsworth diagnosed bronchitis and advised warmth and to stay indoors, it being a very cold winter.

However, they travelled from one house to the other in an open wagon in the cold weather. Over the next few days Chang got worse. He was short of breath if he lay down and so sleep was difficult – difficult also for Eng, although he remained healthy. At four o'clock on the morning of 17 January, fifteen-year-old William, one of Eng's sons, looked into the twins' bedroom and found Chang dead and Eng asleep. The household was awakened. Eng was distressed but remembered that the doctor had promised separation if one died, so someone was sent to fetch the doctor. Eng complained to his wife that he was very "bad off" with pain and distress, especially in his limbs. He requested his wife and children to massage his arms and legs but, before Dr Hollingsworth arrived, he sank into a stupor and died about two hours after Chang's death. His last words were, "May God have mercy on my soul." Dr Hollingsworth gave as his opinion that Chang had died of pneumonia and Eng of "shock and terror inspired by such a union with death". The doctors wanted to perform an autopsy but the wives refused. They realised that burial would entail the risk of the bodies being stolen, so the doctors suggested the bodies be sold. The wives wanted to wait for their eldest children to arrive before making any decision; the two eldest boys were in western USA so would take a long time to return. The bodies were placed in an airtight coffin and buried in a cellar. Soon offers to buy came in but were rejected.

The wives accepted an offer to inspect the bodies from Dr William Pancoast, Professor of Surgical Anatomy at Jefferson Medical College of Philadelphia. The wives gave permission for an autopsy on the following conditions: an incision could be made on the posterior surface of the band but they insisted it should not be divided. There should be no incisions on the heads or faces. In other words, their bodies should not appear mutilated. The bodies were to be kept in a guarded fireproof building. Pancoast accepted these conditions. He and two colleagues duly arrived at Eng's home fifteen days after the deaths. On opening the airtight coffin the bodies were found to be in good condition. Photos were taken and the bodies embalmed. Incisions were made but the doctors decided to complete the autopsy at the Mütter Museum of the College of Physicians in Philadelphia.

Dr Pancoast and Professor Harrison Allen completed the autopsy. On 18 February they reported to a special meeting at the College of Physicians of Philadelphia, at which several experts were present. The bodies were present and were inspected by the audience. Pancoast and Allen described how the two livers were joined together in the band. The band also contained cartilage and a pouch of peritoneum from each twin which did not communicate. Injection of dye into a blood vessel of Chang was found to flow through the joined livers into Eng. One may speculate that there was only minimal mixing of the blood of each twin because it is recognised that when Chang was inebriated with alcohol it had no effect on Eng.

The report was followed by a discussion. There remained some uncertainty as to the cause of death. It had been supposed that Chang died of pneumonia but there was strong evidence of a cerebral vascular clot. Eng's bladder was full and one testicle was retracted, findings that were thought to suggest he had died of fright. The doctors concluded that the decision by most of the surgeons consulted not to operate during life was correct but that separation after Chang's death may have saved Eng's life because the separation could have been made through Chang's part of the band. They could have been safely separated today. There was discussion as to whether conjoining is due to there being two fertilised ova in the same ovarian follicle or whether it is due to fusion of two embryos. Later on, Dr H. H. Newman, an acknowledged expert on twins, pointed out that, as conjoined twins are always of the same sex, the conjoining could not be due to two fertilised ova. He believed the condition to be due to incomplete fission of a single embryo. Division or fusion is still debated today (see Chapter 10).

The twins' marriages had lasted thirty-one years. Sarah, Eng's widow, lived eighteen more years, dying in 1892. She is buried near Eng's farm. Adelaide lived for another forty-three years, dying in 1917 aged nearly ninety-four. When Adelaide died the family decided to reinter the twins together with Adelaide in the graveyard of White Plains Baptist Church which the wives had attended for many years. Margaret, great-granddaughter of Chang, brought the Bunker's chair to an antiques roadshow in South Carolina. This chair (or a similar one) is in the Mütter Museum. In 1952, Robert, son of Eng, was the last of the Bunker children to die. Although the Bunkers lived successfully and prospered, they were always living in an atmosphere of racism, with disapproval of their mixed-race marriages.

Alice Dreger reports that some of the descendants have been worried that their twin ancestors were of Chinese lineage and may have been anxious about a recurrence of conjoining. The latter, however, is extremely unlikely.

Dr Pancoast reflected deeply on the ethical issues posed by Chang and Eng and their families. He discussed his thoughts in his report on the surgical considerations. He seems to have been ambivalent regarding the morality of sex in the presence of another person, as was the case with the twins. He wrote, "Though it seems most immoral and shocking that the two should occupy the same marital couch with the wife of one, yet so thorough was this understanding of alternate mastery, that as I was told by one of the widows, there never had been any improper relations between the wives and brothers." When Pancoast tried to persuade them to have surgery he may have had both medical and moral motives. He added, "They had learned to accommodate themselves to their situation and probably they regarded themselves as equally, if not more favourably, suited in respect of the necessities of life than if they had enjoyed a separate existence." He also observed, "Should a case occur again, I would recommend the operation and be willing to perform it, even if one of the children died, for then at least the survivor would be able to enjoy a natural life. Even if both perished, the risk might be justified; the moral sense of the community, at least in a Christian country, would then not be shocked…"

Bunkers with wives and 18 of their 21 children. Also, bottom right, holding child, is former slave Grace Gates, known as Aunt Grace. Ronald G Becker Collection of Charles Eisenmann. Photo: Research Centre, Syracuse University Libraries.

What is the legacy of the most famous of all conjoined twins? It has been estimated that they have had at least 1000 descendants, with twins only occurring again after four generations, none of them conjoined. They changed the way in which society viewed people with physical differences, encouraging greater acceptance. They showed that many of those who are different can have relatively normal lives with jobs, spouses and children and, above all, can be accepted by society, even though somewhat reluctantly. Prior to the American Civil War, some saw the twins as a symbol of the unity that should exist in their drastically divided nation. Others saw the twins as monstrous and unnatural, as a symbol of division. In 1830, Massachusetts Senator Daniel Webster made a speech against the separatists in Congress in which he called for "Liberty and Union, now and forever, one and inseparable" – surely a reference to the twins. Indeed, the words were quoted when the twins were being advertised. They gave the term 'Siamese twins' to our language. We can speculate about the roles that nature and nurture played in their remarkable lives, a topic examined in Chapter 13.

Epilogue

The joined livers were kept by the Mütter Museum in Philadelphia, together with the lungs and other organs. The livers are preserved there, together with a cast of the bodies, but the fate of the other organs is not known. Both twins left their possessions to their wives. There are no artworks or photographs of the livers. Descendants of the twins have requested that the liver be properly interred but this has been refused so far.

It is highly appropriate that a statue has been erected to the twins' memory close to their original home in Thailand. This was unveiled in 1994 at Tambon Lat Yai on Ekkachai Road, around 4 km from City Hall. It stands in the middle of a broad area decorated with trees and flowering plants. There is a large pond in the foreground. There is also an exhibition.

In the early 1980s, Warren and Nancy Bunker Atkins of North Carolina began Bunker family reunions that have been held every year since. They are held at Mount Airy, North Carolina, near Winston-Salem. This is near the original home of the twins. Nancy is a great-great-granddaughter of Eng Bunker. The events have become large and enthusiastic, which serves to unite many of the numerous descendants of the twins. About a hundred people usually attend, though there may be at least as many as 1000 descendants alive now. Some special friends become honorary non-consanguineous Bunkers. A play by Burton Cohen entitled *The Wedding of the Siamese Twins* is performed. There is a banquet and members can visit Chang and Eng's grave at White Plains Baptist Church. There is a service at the First Baptist Church. The Ambassador of Thailand usually attends. Will Bunker's house is at the present-day site of Mayberry Campground, where participants can visit the former home of Eng and Sarah Bunker's son and see artifacts. The gathering of so many descendants has facilitated and encouraged genealogical research. At the 2002 reunion, Jessie Bunker Bryant, a great-granddaughter of Eng and Sallie, presented her book of the family genealogy.

Bunkers' and wive's tombstone, though Sallie was buried on Eng's farm.

Aunt Grace, former slave and employee of the twins, is buried in the same cemetery as Chang and Eng. In 2003, Grace's descendant, Brenda Ethridge, attended the reunion and was made an honorary Bunker.

Zack Blackmon, Jr., great-great-grandson of Eng, who has attended all twenty-five reunions, said, "That's what this whole reunion is about: forging connections with family members and keeping the Twins' history and memories alive. We're here celebrating today because of them and, of course, we're extremely proud of our heritage."

Non-fiction books about the Bunkers

Duet for a Lifetime. The Story of the Original Siamese Twins by Kay Hunter (1964)

The author is descended from Robert Hunter, the Scot who discovered the twins in Siam.

Book cover description: "She has been able to unearth much hitherto undisclosed material, including illustrations, not only from her own family sources but from the descendants of Eng and Captain Abel Coffin, the villain of the piece who sought to rob the Twins of their earnings."

The Two: A Biography by Irving and Amy Wallace (1978)

Of all the biographies, this one provides the most detailed information.

Book cover description: "*The Two* is a biography of two remarkable lives, astonishing in its extraordinary descriptions of the brothers' triumph over their handicap and fascinating in its exploration of just how the Siamese twins lived."

Chang and Eng Reconnected: The Original Siamese Twins in American Culture by Cynthia Wu (2012)

Leslie Bow, University of Wisconsin, wrote, "*Chang and Eng Reconnected* is a gem with sharp, original, and unexpected twists. What is refreshingly absent here is the traditional use of Chang and Eng as evidence of the cultural fascination with bodily deformity and the sideshow."

Susan Schweik, University of California, wrote, "Wu's far-reaching and often brilliant analysis intertwines Asian Americanist and disability studies to focus attention on forms of political representation in/of the United States."

The Lives of Chang and Eng: Siam's Twins in Nineteenth-Century America by Joseph Andrew Orser (2014)

Book cover description: "… in life and death, the brothers were seen by most Americans as monstrosities, an affront they were unable to escape. More than a biography of the twins, the result is a study of nineteenth century American culture and society through the prism of Chang and Eng that reveals how Americans projected onto the twins their own hopes and fears."

Ann Fabian, Rutgers University, wrote, "His book gives us a compelling account of the changing racial and cultural landscapes of the United States in the nineteenth century…"

John Kuo Wei Tchen, New York University, wrote, "Orser gleans fresh details about their work and reception as they toured, helping us understand the decisions they made and what they endured as self-promoting curiosities in a commercially driven racialised culture."

Fiction or semi-fictional books about the Bunkers (reviewed in Chapter 15)

The Siamese Twins: A Satirical Tale of the Times by Edward G. Bulwer (1831)

Chang and Eng by Darin Strauss (2000)

God's Fool by Mark Slouka (2002)

Chapter 3

Millie and Christine McKoy – nineteenth century

"A soul with two thoughts. Two hearts that beat as one"

"Although we speak of ourselves in the plural, we feel as one person"

"Two strange lumps of humanity"

– The McKoy sisters

Tough beginnings

Millie and Christine McKoy were born in Columbus County, North Carolina in 1851. Their parents, Monemia and Jacob McKoy, were both black slaves. Thus they were born with a quadruple handicap: they were black, slaves, female and conjoined. The lower part of their spines was joined so that they were virtually back to back (pyopagus). How would they cope? Their delivery was reputed to be easy and was conducted by Aunt Hannah, a slave midwife. Christine, the biggest twin, was born first. Together, the twins weighed 17 lbs. Millie was much smaller, although she soon caught up, but remained slightly smaller. Monemia and Jacob already had five boys and two girls, all of them physically normal. More siblings were to follow. Because of their value in the showground, there followed an undignified and cruel tug of war for custody of the twins. The evil of slavery and the avarice of their owners would determine their fate. In 1852, when the twins were ten months old, their parents' owner, Jabez McKoy, a blacksmith and farmer, sold them for $1000 to John Pervis on condition that 25% of the proceeds of exhibiting them, and 25% of the proceeds if they were sold, should be remitted to Mr McKoy. Monemia was allowed to accompany them but, if the twins were sold, she should be returned to Mr McKoy. The following year they were sold to Mr Brower, who borrowed money for the purpose from Joseph Smith. The sum paid was variously reported as $10,000, $30,000 or $40,000. Only a week after his purchase, Mr Brower advertised:

> *Great Attraction! The Celebrated Carolina twins will be exhibited at Raleigh during the Agriculture Fair. These children have been pronounced, for their age, unusually intelligent. They are joined together at the back by the union of the two spines making the connection much more intimate than that of the Siamese twins…*

The Fair was a huge success; entrance was twenty-five cents, with an extra twenty-five to see the twins, who played happily although they could argue and come to blows. Men and women would have had to view the twins separately. Four to six thousand people attended. At the conclusion of the Fair, Monemia was forced to give the twins up. Born into slavery, a career in show business would eventually bring prosperity to them.

They continued to be exhibited in many towns. At each one they would be examined by the local physicians, probed and pinched and then pronounced genuine. At New Orleans the doctors declared them "Nature's greatest wonder". Here a Texan purchased the twins from Mr Brower, promising to pay him with the deeds to valuable land. The deeds and the land didn't exist; the Texan was a swindler. The twins, who were now technically escaped slaves, were taken to Philadelphia. Brower sought them in vain. On hearing of these events, Monemia was heartbroken. Brower being unable to pay up, Mr Smith became responsible for paying the original owner, Mr McKoy. This he did, thus purchasing the twins and, at the same time, the rest of the McKoy family. Smith hired Mr Vestal, a private investigator, to continue the search for the twins.

The twins later claimed that their abductor kept them secret from the public but made money by exhibiting them to scientific bodies. They were then sold on to another man who placed them in a museum in Philadelphia.

In 1854, aged three years, they were exhibited at Mr Barnum's famous American Museum in New York, where the posters declared them "The Latest Novelty". They were also wrongly described as "The Celebrated African United Twins". They were, of course, not African. The twins made friends with other exhibits. A medical report that year stated that the lower third of their sacrums were joined. Detective Vestal, still

McKoy twins.

49

searching, eventually followed the trail to New York but was too late – they had gone. Then, at Newark, New Jersey, he was told that the twins had embarked, bound for Liverpool.

In fact, two showmen, William Thompson and William Millar, the latter known as Professor Millar (but not a true professor), had bought the twins in Boston. A Cuban nanny was engaged. Thompson and Millar were afraid that the authorities may apprehend the twins as escaped slaves and return them to the slave-owning South. To avoid this they were taken to Montréal in Canada, where they were exhibited, and then to Québec. Here also they were alleged to be African. Subsequent events are uncertain, as accounts are confusing. Under the care of Thompson and Millar they sailed in 1855 from Québec. Millie-Christine had successfully escaped slavery and exploitation in the USA but would life be any better in England?

At Liverpool, Millar invited medical men and the press to view the twins at the Waterloo Hotel, where they were intimately examined. They were exhibited in Liverpool as "The United African Twins". The *Liverpool Chronicle* declared them to be "a natural wonder… which far exceeds the interest and curiosity of the celebrated Siamese twins". The *Albion* publication declared them to be "natives of some country up the River Congo". The *Liverpool Daily Post* reported a curious premonition of future nomenclature when the twins objected to being called "niggers", preferring to be called "coloured individuals". Public exhibition was so popular that the intended morning sessions actually lasted all day. One evening there was almost a riot when a spectator shouted that the twins were a hoax, thus provoking booing and hissing. Whereupon a Dr Inman leapt from a box to the stage and declared in a loud voice that he had examined the twins, who were certainly genuine. The boos changed to cheers.

Then to London, where Millar broke with Thompson and absconded with the five-year-old twins and the Cuban nanny to Dundee. The usual routine took place: inspection by medics and then exhibition at Thistle Hall, this time for a shilling. Thompson offered a reward for their recapture, which resulted in their kidnap by thugs he had employed. This involved a physical tug of war with the twins. The police preferred not to interfere, as there were two parties both claiming ownership. Millar was overpowered; his assailants were four prize fighters, who took the twins to London. Thompson took them to court for a custody hearing. The judge asked the twins to talk, whereupon they burst into song with 'O Susannah'. In London, further medical examination established that all internal organs were double and separate and that there were two nearly complete sets of external genitalia. Thompson exhibited the twins in London and around England, claiming that he was raising money to free their slave parents. He pretended that they came from an African town, which he called Tambo, which doesn't exist.

Meanwhile, Millar asked his brother in America to find the twins' parents, which he did. In order to regain custody, the brother and Joseph Smith brought Monemia to Liverpool, landing on New Year's Day 1857. The next day they met Millar in Birmingham, where the twins were being exhibited at a theatre on New Street. Millar informed the police, who accompanied the Millar brothers, Smith and Monemia into the theatre. When Monemia demanded to have her twins a big commotion developed as Thompson tried to drag them away. The police, who had entered disguised as ordinary civilians, promptly took charge of the twins and restored them to their mother. Thompson then went to court, demanding return of the twins. In the court, Thompson had persuaded a black woman to pretend to be the twins' mother and so steal them from their true mother. Monemia shouted, "My own child, O! Give her to me." However, the judge did not believe the imposter and, on seeing Monemia, declared her to be the lawful parent. A court official is alleged to have said, "At least one of them is Monemia's daughter [laughter in court]". The exhibitor tried to drag the twins away but an honest Scotsman barred the way, declaring, "Ye'll nae tak' the bairn ayant the door, maun ye wallop me first, and I'm nae thinkin' ye'll soon do that." Thompson, defeated, offered Monemia £1000 if she would stay in England and allow him to manage the twins until they were eighteen years old. She refused and decided to remain with Millar.

Monemia wanted to return to America but was persuaded to exhibit the twins in Edinburgh, where they were examined by eminent doctors including James Young Simpson, who had also examined the Bunker twins, and James Syme, Professor of Surgery and inventor of the amputation of the ankle now known as Syme's Operation. They considered surgical separation of the twins to be too dangerous.

When advertising the twins in Edinburgh, Millar wished to emphasise their pretended origin in Africa by means of a poster in which they and their mother were surrounded by palm trees. The poster also provided Africanised names for the twins, namely Christine and Millie Makoi, but this time acknowledging their birth in Columbus County, North Carolina. The proceeds of the exhibition would go towards gaining the release from slavery of the rest of their family. James Young Simpson arranged for the twins to attend a lecture at the Obstetrical Society of Edinburgh, where they were again closely examined. There was yet one more event in Edinburgh: Monemia was delivered of another baby, a sister for the twins called Elvy.

Millar wanted to take the twins to mainland Europe. He had ambitious plans, which displeased Monemia as she wanted to return home to America. Suddenly the twins and their mother and Smith disappeared. They were on a train to Liverpool, where they embarked for America. Millar was thwarted; he had no option but to accept defeat. Thompson followed them to America in a vain attempt to regain the twins, now aged six years. When he turned up, his claim to the twins was ridiculed and he was also recognised as an unwelcome abolitionist. According to the *Western Democrat*, the local people sent him packing with the instruction "not to show his ugly physiognomy in these parts again". The paper further commented, "Monsieur Thompson had reason to congratulate himself that he escaped without a coat of tar and feathers!" The Thompson affair resulted in a ditty:

Massa Tomsin run a race;
Oh! Ho! O-o-o yah!
He beat the fastest hoss in de place;
Yah, oh yah! O ha!

Reunited with Mrs Smith, the twins later wrote, "It was a joyous night when we arrived there and found our white ma, Mrs Smith, waiting to secure us". In 1858, the Smiths exhibited the twins on a tour to New Orleans where young Samuel Clemens, later known as Mark Twain, must have seen them. Years later Twain wrote his satirical novels about conjoined twins (see Chapter 15). Then up the Mississippi to St Louis and along the Missouri river to St Joseph. At stopping places the twins would have seen shackled slaves waiting for a boat going south. At this time the future American President, Abraham Lincoln, was campaigning for the Senate, saying, "I believe this government cannot endure permanently half slave and half free."

The twins both learnt to play the piano, or rather two pianos, set at a right angle. In 1858, the Smiths moved to Spartenburg, South Carolina. In 1860, South Carolina and other Southern states seceded from the Union. Civil War was brewing. Showbiz collapsed and business declined. Several of the Smiths' relatives were killed in the Civil War.

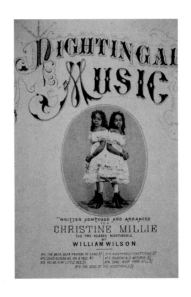

Cover of music for McKoy twins.
Courtesy Professor Bernth Lindfors, Austin, Texas. USA.

Mr Smith, Sr. died in 1862 aged forty-seven. The twins were eleven when they mourned his loss. They later wrote, "He, with a goodness of heart, which in after life developed itself in more ways than one towards us, ascertained where our parents were, went to their owners, purchased them, and all our little brothers and sisters, thus bringing a long separated family together..." The appraisers of his will valued the twins at $25,000 but overall there was a debt that could only be cleared by the sale of many slaves. In 1863, President Lincoln declared all slaves to be free, but the Civil War did not end till 1865.

Freedom and showbiz

There was to be no more slavery for Millie-Christine or their parents, but freedom for the twins was to prove elusive. The twins lived with Mr Smith, Jr. and his family in North Carolina, perhaps even regarding them as additional parents.

Mrs Smith taught them to read and write, together with skipping, dancing and singing, and they learnt to make their own clothes. They proved to be intelligent and willing pupils. Mr Smith, Jr., who was a Methodist Church steward and teetotaller, was reputed to be a kind 'parent' but was keen to exploit them in showbiz. There is evidence that in 1865, at the end of the Civil War when slavery was abolished, the twins' parents wanted to take them away from the Smiths but were refused. Probably the Smiths wanted to continue to profit from the twins' earnings. The McKoys were persuaded to sign a new contract with the Smiths but the next year they were again attempting to leave.

It had been the custom for the twins to be intimately examined by local doctors at each stopping place. The twins were now aged fourteen years and so, not surprisingly, they forbade any such examination in the future. Mary Smith was still poor so the twins generously agreed to help out by earning again. So, at the age of fifteen years, they appeared at Saratoga in Baltimore, Washington DC and other places. They joined with the Bunker twins on the same bill in New York and Hamilton, Ontario. Later they joined Barnum's museum in New York. By this time they had begun to menstruate and were 4 feet 5.5 inches tall. Their style of walking had resulted in their two outer legs becoming larger and stronger than their inner ones. A Professor Charles Lee examined them superficially but was annoyed that he was not allowed to see them naked. They had only been ill once, with fever, perhaps it was malaria.

At the age of seventeen or eighteen years they wrote a thirty-two-page booklet entitled *The History of the Carolina Twins*, told in "Their Own Peculiar Way" by "One of Them". Doubt has been cast on the historical reliability of this document. There may have been a medical section, namely a reprint of the report made by Dr George Fisher in 1868. Strangely, the booklet includes a description of a visit to Queen Victoria at Osborne House on the Isle of Wight but the Royal Archives make no mention of it. However, the visit is described in some detail. They comment, "… She [the Queen] talked tenderly to us, and to our mother and when we left we bore away abundant tokens of her good feeling and queenly liberality." They also comment, "We wish to be viewed as something entirely void of humbug – a living curiosity – not a sham gotten up to impose upon and deceive people… we have been examined most scrutinizingly by too many medical men to be regarded as humbugs by anyone. Still there are many persons who will not believe anything." It is clear that, in spite of their deformity, the twins appeared remarkably content, were willing to exhibit themselves and pleased to be the means of financially supporting their family and associates. The booklet includes the following: "One thing is certain: we would not wish to be severed, even if science could affect a separation. We are contented with our lot, and are happy as the day is long." A song that they composed and frequently performed included these verses:

Some persons say I must be two;
The doctors say this is not true;
Some cry out "Humbug" till they see,
Then they say "Great mystery!"

Two heads, four arms, four feet,
All in one perfect body meet;
I am most wonderfully made,
All scientific men have said.

I'm happy, quite because I'm good;
I love my Saviour and my God;
I love all things that God has done,
Whether I'm created two or one.

It is interesting to observe that the whole song uses the first person singular. Did they regard themselves as one person? However, they were obviously two virtually complete persons and so are referred to as such in this chapter.

In 1869, Dr John Barnard Swett Jackson, Professor of Morbid Anatomy at Harvard Medical School, tried very hard to persuade the twins to accept a full examination. They refused. That same year they toured New England but declined to visit the South again because of reports of high costs and continuing atrocities against blacks. A newspaper printed a tongue-in-cheek quip: "There was one man who courted her successfully, as he thought, for a time, but before popping the question he kissed one face first, and could never get the consent of the other head. She is now waiting till a two-headed man comes along, and is gay with hope."

In 1871, Dr William Pancoast, surgeon at Philadelphia Hospital (who would later perform an autopsy on the Bunker twins), persuaded Millie-Christine, with difficulty, to have a semi-nude photograph taken to appear in his book *Photographic Review of Medicine and Surgery*. It is the only picture of the twins that I have seen in which they do not look happy, so they would probably have preferred it to have no more publicity. One of them looks towards the camera with an angry expression. Dr Pancoast was consulted about an abscess near the anus of one of the twins. He concluded that this was some sort of fistula, the remains of a second anus. His inspection of this problem enabled him to subsequently make the following description: they shared one vulva and one anus, but had separate urethras and bladders; the labia majora, although connected to two clitorises, ran continuously across the vulva and protected but one vagina and one uterus. Having made this intimate examination he invited six other doctors to examine them likewise to confirm his findings. One can easily imagine the distress this must have caused the twins. With regard to future marriage, Dr Pancoast commented that, "Physically there are no serious objections but morally there are insuperable ones." He also predicted that, "… if either Millie or Chrissie shall die first, the other will succumb almost at the same moment".

A subsequent publication was accompanied by two engraved illustrations based on Pancoast's descriptions. The first illustration shows the twins lying naked on a bed, their legs splayed, apparently about to receive a pelvic examination. The second illustration is a stylised line drawing of the twins' vulva. These illustrations can still be found online but are clearly lascivious and in bad taste. A publication of 1889 showed an illustration copying the semi-nude photograph but with the face of one of them turned away instead of looking angrily at the viewer. This modification of the photograph could have been done to prevent readers from realising that the twins were coerced into agreeing to the photo. In 1871 a book was published called *Biographical Sketch of Millie-Christine, The Two-Headed Nightingale*, which records the names of numerous doctors who had examined the twins. There were also many others in several countries.

The frequent intimate medical examinations, together with Dr Pancoast's detailed description and the semi-nude photograph and nude drawings, were possible because the twins were firstly black slaves and, later, freed slaves. There was an unfortunate prurient interest in these vulnerable girls that facilitated their exploitation. Medical discourse was deliberately used to ward off charges of pornography, even while it was used to titillate. It is to their credit that, from the age of fourteen, they discouraged any intimate examinations, in spite of considerable persuasion from doctors.

Europe again

After two months of successful shows in Philadelphia, Millie and Christine sailed again from New York for Liverpool. They were nineteen years of age. In Liverpool, a newspaper commented, "We can testify that no person of ordinary intelligence can be in her company for half an hour without yielding to the charm of her manner and the fascination of her double smiles. She has you on both sides. If you remove your head from one position, you are immediately the victim of another pair of eyes, which fix and in fact transfix you." Another paper stated, "… two young ladies rolled into one, who is certainly a rival to the famous Siamese Twins and very much more attractive in appearance than Messrs Chang and Eng. Her costume was styled low on the back so visitors could see the upper portion of the dorsal connection, and it was done without any infringement of modesty."

The book *Biographical Sketch of Millie-Christine, The Two-Headed Nightingale* included a description of the girls: "Each has a pair of sparkling black eyes which are constantly lit up by intelligence, at which, at any outburst of fun or humour, seem to literally dance with glee; while each mouth is adorned with such a set of brilliant ivory, as an American dentist observed, that many of his patients would be glad to purchase for twenty-five thousand dollars. The sisters were never lonely for each had at all times an intelligent and interesting companion." The book explained, "It may be mentioned as an interesting fact, illustrating the vicissitudes of life and fortune, that the father of Millie-Christine was at one time the slave of a planter named McKoy, and that at this moment he is the owner of the plantation upon which he was once a slave."

The twins explained their devotion to Mrs Smith: "We can trust her, and what is more we feel grateful to her and regard her with true filial affection. We will not go with anyone else; where she goes there we will go; where she tarries there we will halt." This statement is reminiscent of the words of Ruth in the Bible, which the twins may have recalled (Ruth 2.16). The newspaper *La Crosse Democrat* summed up the impression made by the twins: "We have no hesitation in declaring them to be the most extraordinary exhibition of a peculiar and 'indissoluble union' we have ever witnessed. The Siamese Twins in the way of strange formation cannot bear any comparison to them."

They gave a performance for Queen Victoria and her children at Buckingham Palace. The Queen presented them with a matched pair of diamond-studded hair clips. The Princess of Wales gave them brooches. They then performed at the Crystal Palace, which was followed by a tour of Great Britain that included Liverpool and Edinburgh.

In 1872 they sailed for Germany, meeting the Imperial Family at Vienna, Austria. They toured Europe, meeting several other royal families. The next year they were in St Petersburg meeting Czar Alexander II.

There has been much speculation as to the cause of conjoined twinning, a subject dealt with in Chapter 10. However, a frivolous suggestion was made by a gossipy Paris magazine: "All that we know at present is that 9 months before their birth their father dozed off in the middle of a conversation he was having with his wife, woke up two minutes later, and not remembering at just what point he had stopped, he began the phrase all over again!" When they visited Paris, several eminent doctors expressed disbelief that the twins were genuinely conjoined. The twins refused another full examination but one of the doctors was allowed to see only the join at their backs. During their seven years in Europe they visited several countries and were reputed to have learnt to speak French, German, Italian and Spanish.

United States again
They returned to the USA in 1878. They appeared at Philadelphia and then travelled widely in the West, and then went to Cuba. Back at New York they joined Bunnell's Museum. In 1882, at the age of thirty, they wanted to retire and could easily have afforded to do so. However, John Doris of Batchelor and Doris's Great International Railroad (Inter-Ocean) Show strongly urged them to join. They refused, and so Doris asked for their terms. Thinking to dissuade him they said, "$25,000 for the season plus expenses." To their surprise he said, "Yes." So for the first time in their long showbiz career they joined a circus, where for thirty-five weeks they appeared twice a day for six days a week. They were advertised as "The Two-Headed Lady, the Double-Tongued Nightingale, the Puzzle of Science, the Despair of Doctors, the Dual Unity... Only one living creature is like Millie-Christine, and her name is Christine Millie." They would enter the ring, sing and dance a polka and conclude with graceful bows to the audience.

There arose a bitter dispute with the rival Great Forepaugh Show circus as their respective tours tended to coincide. Forepaugh put out many copies of a leaflet (called a rat sheet in those days) maligning the Inter-Ocean Show. A leaflet described the twins as "The Double Headed Darkey they advertise so extensively is the same they have carted around the country for years gone by, and exhibited for 10 cents, when they want 50 cents to see a dark skinned monstrosity. A disgusting sight for ladies and children to gaze upon." Another referred to "A horribly repulsive Negro monstrosity… No lady would knowingly look upon it, little children cover their faces with their hands when encountering this frightful malformation, and the sooner this hideous human deformity is hid from public view the better it will be for the community." The attacks proved fruitless. The twins sued Adam Forepaugh for libel, demanding $25,000. Others were already suing him. He and Barnum were frequently suing each other. Two years later the twins' action was settled in their favour out of court.

The twins continued with Inter-Ocean into 1883, when they were advertised as the "8th Wonder of the World". By this time the twins had become wealthy. They established a splendid home in Columbus County, North Carolina, a home with between ten and fourteen rooms. Their parents and several of their brothers and sisters lived nearby. The parents were able to buy the farm that had belonged to their former slave owner. They established a school for black children, built a church for them and also donated to other colleges. In 1884 they were off to England again, and spending a year visiting the Prince of Wales (the future King Edward VII) at Marlborough House. It is worth noting that artistic impressions of the twins always show them as much slimmer than in some photographs. Back in the USA, their appearances included Barnum's Circus and Lit's Circus in Milwaukee. The twins' father, Jacob, died in 1891 at the age of seventy-nine. P. T. Barnum died the same year. The *New York Evening Sun* printed Barnum's obituary two weeks before his death so that he could read it himself! That year the twins were forty and they celebrated by acquiring matching gold rings with garnets, to be worn for the rest of their lives. The McKoy and Smith families continued close friendships. The twins were regarded as aunts to several Smith children.

In 1909 their house and its precious contents were destroyed by fire, but no one was injured. The house was replaced by another, more modest, building: a six-room cottage. They had been worshipping at Methodist churches but, in 1912, switched to a Baptist church and were baptised by total immersion.

Conclusion

By 1912, Millie had become very ill, probably due to tuberculosis. The twins made a will. They spent time at a sanatorium, where the standard treatment in those days was plenty of fresh air and rest. There was no improvement, although Christine remained healthy. When it became clear that Millie would die but that Christine would not, Dr Crowell sought the advice of Johns Hopkins Medical College as to what to do when this happened. He was advised that no heroic attempt should be made at surgical separation but that it would be kindest to give Christine high doses of morphia to ease her death. The morality and legality of this concerned Dr Crowell so he sought and obtained permission from the State Governor to follow this advice. Millie died on 8 October 1912, just a week after the twins' sixty-fifth birthday. Christine said, "She passed away as in a dream, a peaceful dream." Morphia was administered to Christine, who died after a few hours. This is an example of euthanasia, although she would probably have died soon in any case. There have been no examples of one conjoined twin surviving the death of the other for more than a few hours.

The twins had wanted cremation so as to thwart grave-robbers and possible transfer to Philadelphia for autopsy, as had happened to the Bunkers, but they were buried in Columbus County. The congregation at the Baptist church overflowed at the funeral.

Two arches marked the grave. The inscription on one included the words, "Millie-Christine, born 11th July 1851, Columbus County, N.C. Child or children of Jacob and Monemia McCoy. She lived a life of much comfort owing to her love of God and joy in following his commands. A real friend to the needy of both races and loved by all who knew her." The other arch read, "They that be planted in the house of the Lord shall flourish in the courts of our God (Psalm 92.13)." Bridging both arches were the words, "A soul with two thoughts. Two hearts that beat as one."

As time went by the cemetery became derelict. In 1969, fifty-seven years after the burial, their remains were reinterred at Welches Creek Community Cemetery, North Carolina, not far from the original burial site, with the former inscription cut into a polished granite headstone. This included the quote from the psalm.

The twins' great-great-nephew, Lloyd Inman, recalled, "She was more than just a circus freak, she was a talented, generous black woman who was one of the greatest black women of her time. She said that when God made her, he gave her two heads and two brains because her responsibility was so great."

At the beginning of this chapter the question was asked: How would they cope with their quadruple handicap of being black, slaves, female and conjoined? Readers can judge; surely the conclusion must be that, as far as was humanly possible, they triumphed but that there could never be complete victory.

A more detailed description of their early life can be found in the book *Early African Entertainments Abroad* by Bernth Lindfors.

Chapter 4

A football substitute and others – nineteenth century

Ritta and Christina Parodi

Ritta and Christina were born on 3 March 1829 in Sassari, Sardinia, to Maria Teresa Parodi, a mother of eight children. Their upper bodies were double but they were single from the waist down. They shared one set of genitals, one anus, one pelvis and one set of legs (parapagus). In the autumn of 1829 their parents brought them to Paris, wishing to exhibit them for money. However, upon arriving in France, the family had no idea how to promote the twins and became increasingly destitute. They initially tried to display the twins publicly but a magistrate forbade this on the grounds of public decency. They made a little income from private visitors but remained impoverished. Unfortunately, constant observation interrupted the twins' sleep and exposed them to chills. Ritta, the weakest, soon contracted bronchitis and died at eight months of age. Christina followed a few minutes later.

Within hours the Académie Royale de Médecine wanted a cast of the body. The anatomists wanted to dissect and did so within days, surrounded by many curious doctors and others. During autopsy, it was revealed that the viscera of the pair were transposed to each other. There were two hearts within one pericardium and the one belonging to Ritta was very deformed. The skeleton and plaster cast of the twins are displayed in the Musée d'Histoire Naturelle, Paris, although other organs that were preserved have since disappeared.

The journalist Jules Janin published a strong condemnation of the anatomists, which contained the words "You despoiled this beautiful corpse." Clearly he viewed the twins with romantic respect and he suggested that they would be a fine subject for a novel. The novel was never completed but he left a synopsis in which the twins lived to be seventeen years old, when Christina fell in love. In fact, their death solved what would have been an impossible existence.

A football substitute

Sometime in the mid-nineteenth century, Professor John King of Toronto, Ontario delivered conjoined twins; their names are not known. Little is known about the birth but the subsequent history is unique. There were two heads and three arms. They were probably stillborn. The specimen was preserved in a jar of alcohol and came into the possession of Dr William Winer, son-in-law of John King. During the famous Chicago fire of 1871, Dr Winer placed it for safety in a tub under the pump of St Vincent's Orphanage.

The most popular and enduring legend maintains that the fire began as Mrs O'Leary was milking her cow. The cow kicked over a lantern setting fire to the barn. The O'Leary family denied this, but stories of the cow began to spread across the city. Mrs O'Leary was a target of both anti-Catholic and anti-Irish sentiment. In 1893 the reporter Michael Ahern retracted the 'cow-and-lantern' story, admitting it was fabricated, but even his confession was unable to put the legend to rest. Although the O'Learys were never officially charged with starting the fire, the story became so engrained in local lore that Chicago's city council officially exonerated them – and the cow – in 1997. Sometime after the fire, a relative of Dr Winer found some boys kicking the body about in the street. It was rescued and presented to Rush College, Chicago.

Myrtle Corbin

Myrtle was born on 12 May 1868 in Lincoln County, Tennessee to William and Nancy Corbin. It was an apparently normal birth. She weighed 10 lbs three weeks after birth. Unlike most other examples of conjoined twins, she had only one name because she had the rare condition of her upper body being single but her lower body consisting of two pelves with two sets of pelvic organs and two sets of legs, the inner legs being very small (cephalopagus).

When she was about five weeks old, she was examined by two doctors: Joseph Jones, MD, and Paul Eve, Professor of Surgery at Nashville University. Their report, dated 16 June 1868, described two complete bodies below the waist. There were two small pelves side by side with two separate sets of external genitalia, two urethras and two rectums. Each inner leg was paired with an outer leg. The doctors commented, "The reality in this case surpasses expectation, and we are of the opinion that this living monstrosity exceeds in its curious manifestation of the powers of nature the celebrated Siamese Twins." They suggested that walking would be difficult and that Josephine was likely to be fertile. They suggested that it may be wise to amputate the inner legs but this was never done.

From the age of one month, her father began exhibiting Myrtle for one dime. She learnt to walk with her two outer legs, but with some difficulty. She was shown by P. T. Barnum at the age of thirteen or fourteen, and was advertised as the "Four-Legged Girl from Texas". She was also exhibited by Ringling Bros and on Coney Island. She was soon earning $450 a week. A pamphlet described her as being as "gentle of disposition as the summer sunshine and as happy as the day is long". Her popularity in this industry was such that other showmen began exhibiting hoax four-legged twins. At the age of nineteen, Myrtle married a Dr Clinton Bicknell.

Dr Lewis Whaley described her thus: "She is about five feet high, has fair skin, blue eyes, and curly hair, and is very intelligent. A stranger, to see her in company, would only think her unusually broad across her hips, and with the carriage usual to one with clubbed foot. I have known Mrs B. since she was a tiny child as the four-legged girl, but never realised the perfect dual development of both external and internal genital organs until she became my patient in pregnancy." Dr Whaley determined that the pregnancy was in the left uterus. According to him, upon being told that she was pregnant in the left uterus, she replied in disbelief, saying, "If it had been in my right side I would come nearer believing you are correct." From this remark, physicians assumed she preferred intercourse on the right side; this fact was commented upon in several subsequent reports. This first pregnancy caused her to become gravely ill, the nature of the illness being unknown. After consulting with colleagues, Whaley decided to perform an abortion eight weeks after his initial examination. Myrtle was reportedly between three and four months pregnant at the time. She recovered and subsequently gave birth to four daughters and one son. She died on 6 May 1928 aged almost sixty.

Photographs available on the internet can be confusing. Some authentic photographs of Corbin as a child with very short inner legs are shown alongside images of another fully grown four-legged woman with four normal-looking legs.

The latter photograph is clearly not of the grown-up Corbin. This adult is in fact another four-legged woman called Ashley Braistle, who is sometimes shown with her husband.

Mina and Minnie Finley

The Finley girls were born on 12 October 1870 in Peru Township, Morrow County, Ohio by vaginal delivery. Labour was rapid and they weighed 12.5 lbs. There were two heads, two arms, a single pelvis and three legs, one of which was a double leg with eight toes (parapagus, dicephalus).

The parents signed a contract with a Mr Brown that allowed him to take the twins on tour for $50 a month. However, the twins were instead viewed at their home for fifty cents a time. This arrangement was defended on the grounds that it kept the crowds away and provided money that would be needed for the care of the twins. Many photographs were also sold. Later, the twins appeared at Burneli's Museum. In 1871 they were demonstrated at Jefferson Medical College. Dr William Pancoast, who also appears in the lives of the Bunker and McKoy twins, was also present. Dr Besse became their agent and arranged extensive tours throughout the USA. On arrival by ship at Boston on 18 July 1871, Minnie, who had been ill with vomiting, died. Mina, who had been well, died an hour later. They were aged nine months. Dr Besse wrote, "The two souls have passed from one body to the God that gave them this truly wonderful and curious body." An autopsy was performed and the body embalmed. A plaster cast of the twins was made, which is in the Mütter Museum, Philadelphia. An autopsy showed that their spines were fused, there was one bladder, one set of female sex organs and the intestines were fused, leading to a single anus. The bodies were preserved in an alcohol-filled container and buried.

Laloo

Laloo was a boy born in Oovonin, Oudh, India in 1874. He had a parasitic twin attached to his sternum (probably thoracopagus). They toured the USA and Europe and appeared at the Pathological Society in London. The parasite was dressed as a female but must have been male. In 1899 Laloo joined a protest of Barnum exhibits who demanded to be known as prodigies rather than freaks. They were killed in a train accident in 1905 while travelling in Mexico.

Jean Libbera

Jean was born in 1884 in Rome, Italy. A parasitical twin was attached to his body with a rudimentary head buried in his abdomen, the rest of the parasite being virtually normal. An X-ray showed the parasite's head to have a circumference of about 6 inches. He was the fourth child; the third child had a similar condition and died soon after birth. This is the only example I have found of two sets of conjoined twins having the same parents. He travelled with Barnum and Bailey and with other shows. He was happily married and the father of four children, who were perfectly normal. In retirement he returned to Italy.

Jean was examined by leading medical and surgical experts in both Europe and America. In Paris, Professor Ponier presented him to the Surgical Society and he was pronounced to be the greatest anomaly of nature ever known.

In Cologne, Professor Berdenheimer made a very thorough and complete examination, using X-rays, and in his report he declared that there was, imbedded in the normal body, a formation that resembled a rudimentary head; this he claimed had a circumference of about 15 cm. Jean died in 1936 aged fifty-two.

Tocci brothers

Giacomo and Giovanni Battista Tocci were born in Turin, Italy in 1875 or 1877. They were double above the waist but single below, and thus had two heads, four arms and two legs (parapagus, dicephalus). They probably gave Mark Twain the idea to write two novels (see Chapter 15). Their mother, Antonia Mezzano, was nineteen at the time of their birth, and would later go on to have nine more children, all of them normal. The brothers' parents

Advertisement for Tocci brothers.

recognised the birth of the 'two-headed boy' as a potential blessing and gave them to the Royal Academy of Medicine in Turin to be studied and exhibited as early as one month old. They were deprived of a healthy childhood, being constantly transported from city to city, visiting Austria, Germany, Switzerland, England and Poland. In 1891 they went to the USA, where they toured for five years, visiting New York, Boston, Chicago and many other places. They could stand but not walk. They learnt to speak Italian, French and German.

Giovanni was intelligent, talkative and an excellent artist, whereas his brother possessed little or no artistic ability and was quiet and introverted. Giovanni drank a lot of beer, while Giacomo preferred mineral water. One observer considered them to be on good terms with each other and thought them unconscious of any misfortunes connected with their condition. They were able to write, one being right-handed and the other left-handed. The brothers disappeared from public view in the 1890s, returning to their native country, where they retired in 1897, aged about twenty. To keep gawkers at bay they purchased a secluded, high-walled home near Venice. What became of them afterwards is unknown, though it has been claimed that they married sisters. A rumour alleged that they died in 1906, but others reported seeing them in 1911 and 1912, and that they continued to live near Venice. Finally, a French writer called Martin Monestier claimed that they had died in 1940 at the age of sixty-three.

A toy doll of the Tocci brothers was marketed in the USA in 2007. It was constructed of polymer clay and was 17 inches high. It was commissioned by Jamy in Mount Pleasant, South Carolina. Is it bad taste to exploit these tragic twins, even though they are long dead?

Rosa and Josefa Blažek

Rosa and Josefa were born in Skrejšov, Bohemia (modern-day Czech Republic) on 20 January 1878. Labour and delivery were quick and easy. Their pelves were joined (pyopagus). They were alleged to have a single urethra and anus but this seems impossible as photographs show that they both had almost complete bodies.

As the story goes, a superstitious Mrs Blažek consulted a local practitioner of folk medicine to discover the cause of her twins' unusual connection. The medicine woman instructed the Blažeks to withhold food and water from the infant twins for eight days. The parents complied, yet surprisingly they survived; this was viewed as a divine message that the twins had been put on this earth for a purpose.

When the twins were one year old they were exhibited in local fairs. Like many conjoined twins, the sisters had radically different personalities: Rosa was talkative and witty, while Josefa was quiet and introverted. Their American manager, Jess E. Rose, spoke of the twins' differences: "Rosa was the guiding genius of the two. What Rosa would think, Josefa would do; when Rosa became hungry, Josefa would demand food; when Rosa willed to walk, Josefa automatically stepped forward." Although they were described as having below-normal intelligence, it was claimed they learnt to speak English, Russian, Polish and German together with their native tongue. In 1906 Rosa had a bladder stone removed.

They began a stage career at the age of thirteen, which continued for thirty years. They both learnt to play the violin, piano and xylophone and performed throughout Europe and at the 1893 Columbian Exposition in New York.

A pronounced difference between the sisters was Rosa's interest in the opposite sex. Josefa consistently claimed that she disapproved of Rosa's sexual behaviour. It is uncertain whether Rosa married a soldier named Franz Dvorak in 1907. However, in 1909, she became pregnant. In April 1910 she was in labour in the Prague General Hospital. It is said that ice was applied to her abdomen to delay the delivery until the doctor arrived. He arrived late but the delivery of a boy was normal. The boy was named Franzel and both twins breastfed him, although a wet nurse was also employed. Franzel's baptism certificate states that he was illegitimate. European papers teemed with fictionalised accounts of the twins' sexual escapades, describing Rosa as a harlot and maintaining that Josefa was an unwilling victim of her sister's immorality.

As he grew, Franzel joined the twins' travelling show. When he was only eight months old they appeared in Glasgow to extreme public excitement. There were lurid posters showing glamorous twins dressed in see-through pantaloons together with sequined bras that seemed to be about to burst! The reality was quite different as the twins were short and dumpy, and frankly lacked beauty. The sensation-seeking public must have been disappointed. Their agent, Ike Rose, advertised them as a quintet: "A Mother, Sister, Son, Aunt, and Nephew, in the strangest Family Group the World Has Ever Seen." They performed with the Hilton twins in Germany and in Switzerland as the two sets of twins shared Ike as their agent.

In 1911 it was reported that, after a rail journey from Edinburgh to London when they paid for one ticket, there was considerable argument as to whether they should have paid for two. The outcome is unknown. About this time, in Berlin, a warrant for the arrest of one of the twins was issued regarding a breach of contract. They were imprisoned but the innocent twin brought an action for illegal detention. The outcome of this dispute is not known.

After a lengthy court battle, Rosa was allowed to marry Franz Dvorak, even though he was fined for bigamy! He was killed in 1917 while fighting in the Austrian army, but Rosa called herself Mrs Dvorak for the rest of her life. In due course, Josefa also became engaged to marry, but her fiancé died before the wedding could take place.

In 1921 they went to the USA again to perform in Philadelphia, earning $2500 a week. Their performances included 'ladies only' sessions when they wore revealing tights. At Philadelphia they appeared at the World's Museum, then travelled to San Antonio and Fort Worth, then through the Midwest to Canada and back to the USA. They were involved in a dispute and taken to court, where they accused their manager of keeping most of their earnings.

In 1922, when Josefa became sick, doctors failed to agree on a diagnosis; influenza, appendicitis, constipation and jaundice were all mentioned. They were admitted to Chicago's

West End Hospital, where Josefa slipped into a coma amid discussions about separating the twins to salvage Rosa.

As the twins lay dying, they were visited by their brother, Frank, who, it seemed, had his eye on the sisters' fortune. When Rosa also became comatose, Frank took it upon himself to speak for the sisters. He forbade any attempt to separate them, claiming that is what they would have wanted. American papers vilified Frank for refusing to allow an operation that would have given Rosa a chance. A post-mortem X-ray revealed that their spines were too extensively fused for separation to be possible. Josefa died on 30 March 1922, possibly of pneumonia, though intestinal obstruction was also claimed. Rosa died fifteen minutes later.

They had died intestate so their alleged considerable fortune was fought over by their brother Frank and Rosa's son Franzel. The confusion was sparked by the fact that Franzel, for most of his twelve years, had been billed as "the son of two mothers". If this were the case, then both Rosa and Josefa's shares of their fortune would belong to him, with Frank receiving nothing. This was unacceptable to Frank, who ordered an autopsy to determine which sister was the true mother of the child. On 2 April, three days after the twins' deaths, an autopsy was conducted. The doctors found that the twins had separate uteri, which was proof that Rosa alone was the mother of Franz. This is what Frank wanted to hear so that he could inherit Josefa's share of their fortune. However, soon after the twins had been laid to rest in Chicago's Bohemian National Cemetery, the truth about the twins' so-called fortune was revealed: they had but $400 between them. It is thought that their agent, Ike Rose, had escaped to Berlin with the rest of their fortune, which may have been considerable. Their bodies were preserved in formaldehyde but their final resting place is not known.

Radica and Doodica Neik
Radica and Doodica Neik were born in Orissa, India in 1888. A band of cartilage between their chests joined them, in much the same way as the Bunkers (omphalopagus). Their father wanted to separate them himself because the local villagers regarded the babies as a bad omen; instead, they were taken in by a monastery. In 1888, a showman named Captain Colman purchased the girls. He exhibited them in Europe as the Hindoo Twins. They achieved lasting notoriety when Doodica developed tuberculosis in 1902, and Dr Eugène-Louis Doyen of Paris stepped in to separate them, with the aim of saving Radica from the disease.

The teenage twins were successfully separated, but Doodica died the next day. An autopsy determined that she had died of advanced tuberculosis, and not as a result of the separation surgery. Radica had barely noticed being attached to a dead sister. But she also had tuberculosis, and died a year later in a sanatorium in Paris. Dr Doyen had filmed the surgery, and the film was sent on exhibition in place of the twins.

Chapter 5

The performing twins: the Hiltons – twentieth century

England

Daisy and Violet were born on 5 February 1908 in the English seaside resort of Brighton. Their house was a slum and their mother, Kate Skinner, was probably unmarried. The midwife was Mary Hilton, whose daughter, Edith Emily, was also present. The twins were joined at the lower back region (pyopagus). According to the book *Souvenir and Life Story of San Antonio's Siamese Twins, Daisy and Violet Hilton*, by Myer Myers, who was Edith's husband, the joining tissue was about 6 inches in diameter and composed of skin and muscular tissue with no bone, and with blood circulating between the two twins.

It is often a matter of some puzzlement as to how conjoined twins can manage to be delivered vaginally. Indeed, the procedure is fraught with danger. There is the considerable likelihood of obstructed labour due to the physical impossibility of the normal mechanism of labour taking place. The result can be death or injury to mother and/or baby if skilled help is not available. The problem is avoided these days by elective (planned) Caesarean section before labour occurs (see Chapter 11).

It is therefore of considerable interest to read an account of the delivery of the Hilton twins, who were born vaginally without any ill effects. The following is the account given by Dr James A Rooth in the *British Medical Journal* dated 23 September 1911:

The twins were born a few minutes before I arrived… The mother was a young primipara [first baby] aged 21, tall and well built. The labour, as described to me by the nurse, was almost uneventful; it lasted sixteen hours and the pains were strong. The first child was born by a vertex presentation [head first]… and the birth presented no abnormal features; but as the legs were not delivered the nurse examined and found an obstruction which she very naturally took for the breech [bottom first] of the second child, but also could not understand the cause of the obstruction until a few minutes later the feet of the second child came down, and in ten minutes from the birth of the first the second was delivered. The process was evidently one of evolution of the second [by which the baby adapts to the space available by contortion and traction of the joining ligament]… and seems to have been been the method of birth in the few similar cases which are recorded… The children, who are both girls, were well formed and of average size. I judged them to be fully 6 lb each, and a few days later they weighed down the scales at 13 lb".

Understandably Kate was terribly alarmed, even refusing to hold the twins. In those days many people believed that congenital abnormalities were a divine punishment, in this case, perhaps a punishment for Kate's adultery. The identity of the twins' father was never discovered. At first, Mary frequently chided Kate with the accusation that the monster was the result of loose morals but, after a few days, became sympathetic and encouraging. The people of Brighton were also sympathetic, and soon made numerous gifts.

In view of Kate's rejection of the twins, Mary Hilton, with the approval of her husband, adopted them. Their motive could have been simple compassion but, in view of subsequent events, it was probably the anticipation of making money. So it was that the twins acquired the surname Hilton. A Congregational minister at the local Countess of Huntington Church (a non-conformist denomination related to Methodism) baptised them. Mary had kept the twins hidden from the public but she invited a newspaper reporter to the baptism in order to gain publicity. He reported in the *Brighton Herald* that, "They are, as far as is known, the most wonderful couple in the world." As a result, there were many visitors, who were allowed to see the twins on purchase of a twopenny picture postcard of them.

As they grew up they were instructed to address Mary as Auntie, and her succession of five husbands as Sir. The twins later reminisced, "Our earliest and only recollections are the penetrating smell of brown ale, cigars and pipes, and the movements of visitors' hands which were forever lifting our baby clothes to see just how we were attached to each other... in order to find out whether or not there was some trick about our condition." Mary became something of a heroine, being praised in sermons and newspapers.

Years later the twins claimed that Mary had never showed them any affection and used to beat them with the buckle of her wide belt. Being examined by various doctors frequently distressed them. The Sussex Medico-Chirurgical

Society, after examining the X-rays, concluded that any attempt at separation would be too dangerous. The twins, recalling the medical examinations, stated, "We were punched and pinched and probed until we were almost crazy, and we always screamed, scratched and kicked. When the doctors and scientists left, Auntie would often whip us and call us ungrateful little brats."

Hilton twins dancing.

From the age of two years the twins were exhibited at various circuses and carnivals around England and Scotland. At this time, the Blažek adult conjoined twins and the eight-month-old son of Rosa Blažek (see Chapter 4) were being exhibited in Scotland. Mary saw these twins singing and dancing in public. This gave her the idea to arrange for the Hilton twins to learn to sing, dance and play musical instruments, which they did from the age of three. Therefore, they were not only exhibited but were also able to entertain, and did so with considerable ability. Various impresarios managed their tours.

Touring

At the age of four the twins toured Germany, where doctors in Berlin thought that separation would be possible, but Mary refused, to the delight of the twins, who feared surgery. For a while they performed on the same bill as the Blažek twins in Germany and Switzerland.

Next stop was Melbourne, Australia, at the age of five; fifty doctors of the Medical Society of Melbourne examined them.

However, there was much less public interest in Australia, even when they joined a circus which toured the outback and then New Zealand. In 1915, their impresario, Myer Myers, married Mary's daughter, Edith, in Sydney. He then became responsible for the twins but was very strict.

At the age of eight they travelled across the Pacific to the USA where they were detained on Angel Island off San Francisco, where illegal immigrants were held. The health inspector declared them, "physically and biologically inferior". However, newspaper publicity overcame the inspector's scruples and they were soon touring the USA as carnival entertainers. They joined Wortham's World's Greatest Show, being introduced (falsely) as "through the kind auspices of His Majesty King Edward the Seventh of England... Daisy and Violet Hilton, The Royal English United Twins". They were even described as being descended from Queen Victoria, while making a lot of money. A leaflet advertised them as, "These Lovely Girls Happy and Vivacious in Their Inseparably Linked Lives Have Perfected Natural Talents Which Make Them One of the Greatest and Most Meritorious Attractions in the World". After a while they settled in Phoenix, Arizona, where Edith gave birth to a daughter.

In 1917, a twelve-year-old lad called Jim Moore encountered the twins. He described meeting them as follows: "The girls seemed to be glowing, as if there were auras around them. The scene was a little like that in

Hiltons with dance partners.

the movie *Song of Bernadette* where Bernadette comes upon a grotto… and gets a vision of the Virgin Mary." He was certainly smitten and would remain a close friend for a long time. They liked him too, but were rarely allowed near him.

Two years later Mary died; she was sixty-seven years old. She bequeathed the twins to Myer, which the twins reluctantly accepted, though they longed to get away from him and thought about running away. They did not realise that such a bequest was strictly illegal. He kept close control of them, not letting them be seen in public, in order to protect their value as showbiz stars. While Myer continued to make a lot of money, he rejected attempts by Barnum and Bailey and other circuses to sign them up.

In 1922, at the age of fourteen, they underwent extensive psychological testing by Helen Koch. Daisy's test results showed her to have superior intelligence to Violet. They were very different in word association tests and Daisy was more mature emotionally. Tested again in 1932 by Ernest Seeman and Robert Saudek, Daisy liked the romantic literature of Conrad, Sabatini and J. M. Barrie, whereas Violet was more serious and "liked to pit her young mind against the unsolved mysteries of time".

Their fellow performers became concerned at the twins' ill treatment. Myer and Mary had not allowed them to associate with other children or to show themselves outside the tent. Several meetings took place, which led to defiance of the Myers'. A one-day strike took place on 2 July 1924, in which all 350 performers and workers took part. The performers then entertained the twins. For the first time they were able to ride the Ferris wheel and the Ocean Wave and saw the motorcycle daredevils. There were posters proclaiming, "We love you Daisy and Violet." This was the most enjoyable experience of their sixteen years.

At this time they could play the saxophone, clarinet, piano and violin. They could sew and enjoyed detective stories. They learnt to dance. There was a competition to select two young men to be the twins' dancing partners. At the age of about sixteen they would dance with these two young men à *pas de quatre*. The leading entertainment magazine *Variety* described them as "the greatest… attraction and business getter that has hit vaudeville in the past decade".

Soon after their seventeenth birthday, the twins finally appeared at Newark's State Theatre. Their musical director, Ray Traynor, introduced them as "The San Antonio Siamese Twins". The show was such a huge success that their contract for $1000 a week was replaced by one for $2800 a week. The twins then performed in Boston, Cleveland and Buffalo, achieving box office records at each.

The Myers' decided to take the twins to New York in an attempt to conquer Broadway. At first the agents rejected them, claiming freaks belonged in sideshows and not on the big stage. They were also concerned that pregnant women, on seeing the twins, might be afraid that they themselves could be at risk of delivering monsters. Eventually their break came; the owner of a chain of vaudeville theatres had the courage to sign them up. Their Broadway debut came in March 1925, when they were aged seventeen. The *New York Daily Mirror* ran a competition in which children had to colour in a black and white image of the twins each day. The winners were given Daisy and Violet dolls. They auditioned in the Hippodrome, which, with its 5200 seats, was the largest theatre in the world. However, they were so nervous in the huge theatre that they messed up the audition. Myer fumed that he would send them to an asylum. Another promoter, Terry Turner, saved the day. He saw the twins, declaring that their act would need "classing up". So he classed them up for two months and enlisted them with Marcus Leow, who controlled 350 theatres and movie houses in several countries.

The twins sometimes appeared on the same bill as the famous entertainers George Burns, Jack Benny, Eddie Cantor and Sophie Tucker. In 1926 they joined an act with Bob Hope called Dancemedians in which the twins tap-danced.

Hiltons with Myer and Edith Myers.

Daisy learnt to drive; Violet could not do so because she would have been on the right in left-hand-drive vehicles.

They had become the highest-paid performers in vaudeville but, in 1927, Myer, who had become their legal guardian, kept all the money for himself, although he did provide the twins with a luxurious lifestyle. During the 1927/28 season, Daisy fell in love with Don Galvan, a Mexican singer/guitarist who appeared on the same bill. Myer tried hard to prevent this romance, thus provoking the twins to attack him physically. They declared, "… listen, Sir, we are 18 years old. Don't you strike either of us or we'll yell like wildcats! And get us a separate room. We're grown ladies and you should be ashamed to force us to share your and Edith's room!" Myer then agreed to give them regular payments and to grant them much more freedom. Having earned so much, they lived in a palatial house in San Antonio. From about 1928, the increasing popularity of the cinema drastically undermined stage shows, so that the twins found themselves underemployed. Their income dropped from about $4000 a week to $400. Furthermore, two other rival sets of conjoined twins began appearing on stage. They were Mary and Margaret Gibb, and Simplicio and Lucio Godino from the Philippines (see Chapter 6).

Romance and travel

It has been claimed that the twins both fell in love with Bill Oliver, an employee of Myer; he was a married man twice their age but he returned their affection. The *ménage à trois* resulted in jealous arguments between the twins. However, in their book *Intimate Loves and Lives of the Hilton Sisters*, the twins deny any such love affair, although they sent him a photo signed, "with love and best wishes". Not surprisingly, they were devastated to receive a subpoena to appear as co-respondents in a lawsuit brought by Bill's wife, who was demanding a quarter of a million dollars in damages. The *Kansas City Times* had a field day, calling this "the four-sided love triangle". Bill responded by abandoning the twins and his wife. The twins were heartbroken. On top of all this, 1929 arrived, the year of the Great Depression which made employment for the Hiltons virtually impossible. The lawsuit petered out.

The twins' greatest desire was to escape Myer and Edith and gain control of the large sum of money – their earnings – that the Myers' possessed. Therefore, in 1931, they sued the Myers' in court. There was great public interest in the trial so that, when it opened in a huge hall, 700 spectators crowded in. The twins won freedom from their adoption to the Myers' and were awarded $100,000. In triumph they declared, "The don'ts of our childhood were now all do's, and we reveled in it." Indeed, they embarked on a hedonistic lifestyle that included boyfriends, visits to cinemas and nightclubs and enjoyment of alcohol and cigarettes. When one twin had a date the other would just read a book. Surprisingly, Don Galvan turned up, whom Daisy had fallen for in 1928. He proposed marriage to

Daisy, suggesting that they should live together for six months and that then she could go wherever Violet wanted to go for six months. Perhaps he got this idea from the Bunker twins, who spent alternate three-day periods with their respective wives. Although Daisy was deeply in love with Don, she tearfully declined the proposal because of the difficulties she foresaw and eventually lost interest in him.

In 1932 the successful film producer Tod Browning persuaded the twins to appear in an MGM film called *Freaks* which featured a cast of real freaks. The film is discussed in Chapter 15. During their stay in Hollywood they were described in *Motion Picture* as "... more than pretty... They are beautiful. They are exquisitely gowned and groomed. Their hair is beautifully waved and hennaed... clever, sophisticated, well-read and witty." The twins' next adventure was a meeting in 1932 with bandleader Jack Lewis in Chicago. He brought Maurice Lambert along to make up a foursome. Barely two months later, Daisy was engaged to Jack; Violet approved. One newspaper reflected, "It must be something of a feat to keep one twin in love, and the other liking but not loving him... In all the literature of the world there is not a word of advice on how to manage a bride when her sister is present on all occasions." Around this time, Violet sought out Blue Steele, another bandleader, though he was married. That year the twins became American citizens, partly to ensure their re-entry to the USA after a proposed visit to England to find their mother.

The Great Depression lifted, the twins received offers of work, but declined them. They were now aged twenty-three but had never heard from their mother or other relatives. They did know that she had rejected them because she thought their abnormality was a punishment from God. They felt forgiveness for her and wished they could meet her. So they went to England in 1933, arriving in London, where they frequently attended theatres, seeing plays by Shakespeare, Shaw, Molière and Noël Coward, and also prize fights. A newspaper reported that fight spectators became more interested in the twins than the fights. Soon they were back in Brighton, their place of birth, but were devastated to discover that their mother had died in 1912 of the complications of childbirth. They found her grave.

They were soon performing all over Britain with great success, especially at the Brighton Hippodrome. Violet fell in love with the boxer Harry Mason. The next year they returned to the USA, with Harry promising to join them for a double marriage the next year. However, Daisy and Jack then parted and Violet fell for bandleader Maurice Lambert. They formed a touring show called 'The Hilton Sisters and Their Orchestra' with Jim Moore, their long-time friend, as dancer and MC. When Moore was interviewed he was prepared to be surprisingly explicit about his knowledge of the twins' sex lives. He claimed that Violet and Daisy were both nymphomaniacs and that they just couldn't get enough sex. He added that they might see two or three lovers at different times during the same night. There is no confirmation of this.

Violet and Maurice applied for a marriage certificate from the New York Corporation, the acting head of which refused, saying, "The very idea is quite immoral and indecent." Violet was quoted as saying, "I am Violet Hilton. This is my prospective husband, Maurice Lambert. Yesterday we tried very hard to procure a marriage license both in the states of New York and New Jersey, but in both places were refused. I feel very, very unhappy about it because I love Maurice very, very dearly and he loves me and I don't see any reason in the world why we should be denied the pleasure of being happy." Therefore they dashed over the Hudson river to Newark but had no luck there either. They appealed to the New York Supreme Court to reverse the rejection, citing the precedents of the Bunker twins, who had married sisters in the USA in 1834, and the Godino twins, who had married sisters in the Philippines in 1929. The Court turned them down. They tried to get married in twenty-one different states but were always refused. Eventually the clerk at Elkton, Maryland agreed to marry them. They were overjoyed but the clerk was overruled by the state attorney. In the eyes of the public, Maurice became a pathetic laughing stock; he gave up and went to Europe, where he disappeared. There were suggestions that Violet may have been bisexual or even lesbian by inclination, although the latter seems unlikely in view of her efforts to get married. There was never any doubt about Daisy's interest in men only.

In 1936, at the age of twenty-eight, Daisy became pregnant, the father probably being a married musician. Their manager, fearful of losing the twins' considerable earning power, strongly urged Daisy to get an abortion. She reluctantly agreed and consulted a doctor, who refused, as abortion was only legal to save the life of the mother. An illegal ('backstreet') abortion would have been possible but they rejected this, being well aware of the dangers. It is of interest to note that, during the pregnancy, menstruation ceased in both twins, indicating that the blood of each woman and their hormones intermingled. The baby was given up for adoption.

Readers will by now probably be bemused by the tangled love affairs of the twins, who were still only twenty-eight. However, the tale now takes a bizarre turn. A new manager persuaded Violet to get married to their lifelong friend, Jim Moore, in a highly publicised wedding at the Dallas Cotton Bowl. This was to be a genuine wedding but also a publicity stunt! Jim took a lot of persuading but eventually agreed to the plan. Daisy, still being pregnant, was maid of honour. Surprisingly, Texas had granted a permit. The twenty-five-cent admission ticket would provide the spectacle of the wedding followed by music and dancing. In spite of huge publicity, ticket sales were disappointing because there was a big rival show in town featuring nude dancers, the latter being illegal in Dallas but somehow was allowed. With difficulty the twins found a clergyman willing to officiate at their wedding. After the knot was tied he said, "You may kiss the bride." That was rather awkward as Jim was 6 foot 2 while Violet was 4 foot 10! Can anything be added to make this tale more bizarre? Yes! Jim Moore's friends considered him to be gay. The wedding had been on 18 July 1936. Less than two months later, in New Orleans, they filed for annulment on the strange grounds that they had not given valid consent. The annulment was suspended when they left New Orleans and was not finalised until seven years later. The publicity stunt backfired. When the public discovered the truth, the twins' popularity plummeted. Their plight was well described by author Dean Jensen: "Stripped of their innocence, from then on they were *persona non grata* wherever they appeared. The doorman and the desk clerks at their hotel stopped greeting them. In the past they had always been given the choicest tables in restaurants but now they were seated nearest to the kitchen or washroom. The sisters even had trouble hailing taxis. Most cabbies sped right by them." On a train journey, the twins bought only one ticket. The ticket collector telegraphed for advice and was told, "Make no attempt to put one of them off the train!"

Their failure to find much showbiz work and their profligate lifestyle made the twins poor again. They therefore borrowed from friends, and took to excessive drinking. By 1937, they were forced to enter circus sideshows again. A break came in 1939, when they were engaged to entertain on the luxury transatlantic liner the *Berengaria*, which at that time was the largest luxury liner afloat. Their pianist was Buddy Sawyer, who also danced with them. About two years later they found work at Brogan's club in Buffalo, New York. Daisy proposed marriage to Buddy and he accepted. They married in 1941 at a civil ceremony at Buffalo; the marriage of conjoined twins was by now becoming easier. However, it did not last long. Buddy deserted Daisy eleven days later and, in 1944, they were divorced.

In spite of differences, the twins lived peacefully. When aged thirty-five, they remarked, "Sleeping, eating, walking, bathing, and dressing, drinking and making love – we share our lives, just as amiably as we shared our toys without quarreling... It is as though some Power, greater and stronger than ourselves, has given us this inner harmony to compensate for our being forced to live constantly as an entity... In our relationship, neither dominates." Later they complained, "Yet we still long to find real romance and love equal to our own tolerance and forgiveness. We dream of having homes and families (doctors tell us there is no reason why we can't have children)." But they added a note of optimism: "Life has given us plenty of problems, and we have adjusted ourselves to most of them. And somewhere still, we believe and hope we will find the right mates, to whose understanding and love we can entrust our private lives."

They met the famous escapologist Houdini. He became their close friend for many years. They claimed that he taught them how to separate themselves spiritually and emotionally from each other, and thus to overcome their physical constraint to some extent. This would have been a great asset when romantic relationships developed. In fact, they had been flirting and even told a reporter that they were both engaged and would marry in three years' time. The scoop was printed but of course it was a joke. They described themselves: "Daisy is blond and green-eyed, weighs 93 pounds and is five feet tall. Violet has dark hair and hazel eyes, never weighed more than 89 pounds and is four feet 11 inches tall." They claimed to have donated blood.

After the USA entered World War II the twins became poorer as they failed to find suitable work. In 1943, becoming desperate, they agreed to perform in a burlesque show in Philadelphia as "The World's Only Strip-teasing Siamese Twins". This involved partial nudity. To some extent they hid behind their musical instruments. Later, a risqué comedy act involved a man who claimed to be able to make love to both twins at the same time. With his trousers billowing outwards, Violet pulled the waistband to look in, whereupon Daisy took a hairpin and thrust it into the bulge, which exploded with a loud pop. It was of course a balloon gradually inflated via a tube from a concealed bicycle pump!

As the war progressed, the twins performed at rallies organised to sell United States Defence Bonds and thus became popular entertainers again. An amateur hypnotist called L. Daniel Schmidt devised an act with the twins which he hoped would contribute to psychological knowledge. He planned to hypnotise both twins and then examine their psyches to demonstrate how different two people could be even when they shared the same genetics and environment. This experiment took place in the Pittsburgh Variety Club canteen. He even invited the famous psychologist Carl Jung, but only a crowd mostly comprising GIs attended. Schmidt got the twins into an apparent trance using a swinging watch. He then tried to get Violet to recall their first stage appearance at the age of three. She described the famous exotic La Scala opera house at Milan. This was not what Schmidt wanted so he abandoned the show. Later, Violet admitted that she had faked the trance and had described La Scala from pictures she had seen.

The *American Weekly*, a Hearst publication with the biggest circulation in the world, published their life story as a serial, entitled *The Private Lives of the Twins*. In this account the twins changed the names of the main characters of their early life but boldly described their various love affairs, mentioning Bill Oliver, Don Galvan, Blue Steele, Maurice Lambert, Jack Lewis, Harry Mason, Jim Moore, Buddy Sawyer and others. They concluded by declaring their desire for real romance and stating that doctors had told them they could bear children. This resulted in many proposals, none of which impressed them.

In 1943 they appeared at the Club Bali in Miami and at other Florida resorts. This was a success, probably due to the interest generated by the newspaper serial. Then they obtained work in fairs, which involved a lot of travelling. They bought a former driving instructor's car with controls on the right and left. They often slept in the car. In 1951 it was off to Hollywood again to make another film; this time a much more respectable one without a cast of freaks. It was called *Chained for Life*, the plot being based on Mark Twain's short story *Those Extraordinary Twins*, which is described in Chapter 15.

Decline

By 1956, without entertainment work, the twins opened a snack bar, which was also a flop. Then they tried selling cosmetics door to door, which failed to stop them having to borrow money. And so it was back to the stripteasing life again, which they hated. They found a few more poorly paid jobs but became homeless, only managing to survive thanks to the generosity of friends, including one who let them stay in his motel free of charge. In 1959 Daisy developed pain, possibly due to complications of a hernia she had acquired after childbirth. She was operated on at Mount Carmel Mercy Hospital. In 1961 their manager stole their money, so they were stranded in Monroe near Charlotte, North Carolina. The same year they performed in drive-in theatres, in a show that included a film. Then in 1962 they moved to humble accommodation at Charlotte, North Carolina, where they found work as produce-weighers in a big shop. Co-worker Pauline Harton commented on their personalities: "The sisters were as different as day and night. Daisy was warm and friendly and soft and feminine. Violet on the other hand was hard and could be gruff. I really think she hated all men and children." On taking her own twin babies to see the twins, Pauline found that Daisy cooed over them but that Violet took no notice.

In 1968 Daisy caught the Hong Kong flu. A doctor advised hospitalisation but she refused and died at the end of the year or early in 1969, aged almost sixty-one. A few days later the police forced an entry to find both twins dead. No post-mortem examination was made; a doctor certified that both had died of influenza. The minister of the Methodist church they had attended occasionally conducted the funeral. There were twenty-three floral tributes but nothing from the world of showbiz. They were buried at Forest Lawn Cemetery, Charlotte, North Carolina. Probably because a new grave could not be afforded they were interred in the grave of Troy Thompson, who had died of drowning in Vietnam in 1965. The plaque is situated on the ground in front of Thompson's memorial. The Reverend Jon Sills, who conducted the funeral, wrote a rather sad obituary comment: "Daisy and Violet Hilton were in show business all but the last half dozen of their sixty-one years… In the end, though, they were cast aside by the glittery and glamorous world that they had been part of for so long. In the end it was only ordinary people who showed they cared about them..."

Their lives had truly combined triumph and tragedy with an amazing ability to adapt to their disability. However, showbiz had not finished with them. In 1997 a musical called *Side By Side* opened on Broadway, based on their life (see Chapter 15).

Chapter 6

The athletic musicians: the Godinos and others – twentieth century

Simplicio and Lucio Godino

The Godinos were born in 1908 on the island of Samar in the Philippines. A buttock of one was joined to a buttock of the other (pyopagus). Simplicio, on the left in photographs, was right-handed while Lucio was left-handed. At the age of ten they entertained at Coney Island in the USA, although the Brooklyn Society for the Prevention of Cruelty to Children objected. The Commissioner of the Philippines came to the rescue by adopting them. Under his care they were well educated in the USA and the Philippines. In spite of their disability they became proficient at tennis, golf and swimming. They learnt to drive, to play five musical instruments and to speak five languages. Eventually they led a band of fourteen musicians called the All Fillipino Band that toured the world.

In 1929, aged twenty-one, they married sisters Natividad and Victorina Matos in Manila at a Roman Catholic church. The marriage licence clerk objected, claiming that, as they were one person, the marriage would be bigamy. He was overruled by the Department of Justice. When the twins applied for US citizenship, they were told they would first have to serve three years in the Philippine Army, which was obviously impossible.

The two couples performed in vaudeville in the USA. Their act included a salacious portrayal of their lovemaking. This provoked the reviewer of *Billboard* to declare, "To be brutally frank, they are as much out of place as a burlesque show in the chambers of the United States Supreme Court." In spite of this it is not surprising that their shows were very popular. Their act was accompanied by the triple-X film *The Miracle of Birth*.

In 1929, Lucio was prosecuted for driving offences. Simplicio protested to the judge that he should not be punished for his brother's offences. The judge therefore dismissed the case.

In 1936, Lucio died of pneumonia at the age of twenty-eight. Some say it was as a result of rheumatic fever; these were pre-antibiotic days. His brother was unaffected and so, forty-five minutes after Lucio's death, surgeons separated them. Part of Simplicio's large intestine had been in Lucio's body and was merged with Lucio's intestine. This was repaired and Simplicio's intestine was restored to his body. However, he died eleven days later, allegedly of meningitis. It is possible that the psychological shock of losing his brother contributed to Simplicio's death.

Mary and Margaret Gibb

Mary and Margaret were born in 1912 in Holyoke, Massachusetts. They were joined at the base of the spine and had a shared rectum (pyopagus). Their parents refused separation when they were three years old and again when they were sixteen years old. Subsequently the twins themselves also refused surgery. They were educated at home by tutors.

At the age of thirteen they were exhibited at the Wonderland Circus Sideshow on Coney Island. This caused them to be prosecuted on the grounds that they were underage, but it was unsuccessful. As teenagers they gave public performances of dancing and piano playing. Ray Traynor, who had instructed the Hilton twins, found that they lacked entertaining talent. He declared, "Mary and Margaret were no more trainable than jellyfish. I'd arrange a song in the key of G and one of them would sing it in B-flat and the other in D-minor. They weren't any better as dancers." In spite of this they managed to entertain somehow. Their parents accompanied them as they toured Europe in 1930, visiting Paris, Brussels and Switzerland. Back in the USA they joined the Ringling Brothers, Cole Brothers and Barnum and Bailey circuses. In 1933 they appeared at the Chicago World Fair. The magazine *Variety* summed up: "Their playing and dancing pass as well as anyone could want, especially when not much is expected."

Margaret had two operations, one for removal of a bladder stone and the other for removal of a uterine fibroid. They retired in 1941 at the age of twenty-nine and opened a shop which they called the Mary-Margaret Gift Shoppe, which sold novelties, gifts and baby clothes which they had made themselves. At the age of thirty-four, Mary was described as stout and placid while Margaret was thin and highly strung. Both had IQs of eighty. Other tests showed Margaret to have higher-than-average scores on the hypochondriac, depressive and hysteria scales with Mary having normal scores. The Rorschach inkblot test showed anxiety in the case of Margaret. In 1949 they closed their shop and disappeared from public view except for visits to church. They continued their interests in knitting and watching television.

In 1967, at the age of fifty-four, the twins died within two minutes of each other. At that time they were probably the oldest living conjoined twins in the world. An autopsy showed that Margaret had cancer of the bladder, which had spread to the lungs of both sisters. They were buried in Holyoke. Probably they could have been separated but they always steadfastly refused.

Yvonne and Yvette Jones (or McCarther)

Yvonne and Yvette were born in 1949 in Los Angeles. The tops of their heads were joined (craniopagus). Their father was John Jones and their stepfather was Charles McCarther. It was determined that the twins shared too much tissue to be separated safely, so their mother took them home at the age of two years. She was then given a bill for $14,000. The only way to pay was by exhibiting the twins in the sideshow of a circus, earning $300 a week. Doctors predicted that they would never be able to walk and that they would be mentally retarded because of the brain tissue they shared. The twins proved their doctors wrong on both counts. They developed above-average intelligence and were so active physically that their mother was afraid they would break their necks.

They spent many years as successful gospel singers, touring the nation and singing in churches. Although they were not allowed to attend classes in high school, they managed to obtain their diploma through home schooling. For a while they received instruction over the phone but, when that didn't work, the teachers came to their house. In 1987, the twins moved out of their mother's home and into their own apartment. They also enrolled in a community college, with the goal of earning nursing degrees. Sadly, on 1 January 1993, the sisters were found dead in their apartment. It was concluded that they had died of heart disease, as Yvonne was known to have had an enlarged heart. The coroner decided that they had died on 15 December 1992. The sisters' degrees were awarded posthumously at their funeral as a tribute to their extraordinary dedication.

Masha and Dasha Krivoshlyapova

Masha and Dasha were born on 3 January 1950 in Moscow. Labour lasted three nights and two days. They were born vaginally but at least two websites mistakenly claim that they were born by Caesarean section. The girls had joined spines and pelves and three legs, one of which was actually a fusion of their inner legs. They had separate genitalia but shared a uterus, bladder and lower intestine (ischiopagus tripus). They were separated from their mother at birth. Their mother spent a month in hospital recovering and, when she refused to sign forms giving up her parental rights, she was told that her children had died. Their father rejected them, declaring that they could not be his. Soon after the birth the twins were briefly shown to their mother; she never saw them again until thirty-eight years later.

They lived at the Paediatric Institute in Moscow until they were aged six. They were not allowed out of doors before the age of eleven. Until they were six or seven, Soviet scientists subjected them to numerous, sometimes cruel, experiments. No one else was allowed to see them. The doctors wore masks all the time. There were numerous blood tests. One of the twins was packed in ice to see what effect this would have on the other. Another experiment involved burning one twin to see the effect on the other. Gastric juices were obtained by stomach tubes. One twin was starved. Uncomfortable helmets were placed over their heads to facilitate electrical studies of their brains. Dasha said, "But after they had written their dissertations the scientists threw us away and forgot about us." With difficulty they learnt to walk at the age of five. A film can be seen on YouTube made by the Russians entitled

Krivoshlyapova, Masha/Dasha. 'Medical Documentary on Conjoined Twins' (see Bibliography). It shows some of the experiments. This was shown to doctors in London, who were so disturbed that the Russians subsequently edited out the crueller items.

Between the ages of six and fourteen, the twins lived at the Soviet Scientific National Institute for Prosthetics in Moscow, which was an orphanage for handicapped children. Conditions were spartan, with no hot water for example. The twins were pleased to meet children of their own age but, when interviewed on a BBC programme many years later, Dasha complained, "People call us 'two heads'. You hear all sorts of rubbish and it makes us cry." Later, a physiotherapist called Auntie Nadya cared for them.

Between the ages of fourteen and eighteen, they were at the School for Invalids at Novocherkassk, 550 miles from Moscow. In 1964, doctors planned to amputate the third leg. They injected local anaesthetic but Dasha struggled so much that they had to abandon the attempt. In 1968 the third leg was amputated under a general anaesthetic; the twins regretted this because it made walking so difficult that they had to acquire crutches.

Their personalities differed. Masha was more energetic and talkative; she described herself as being the masculine half. She could be aggressive and often hit Dasha, who was more serious and passive and was an alcoholic. Dasha suffered from stuttering from the age of fourteen. They both smoked and consumed vodka, sometimes getting drunk. Many years later, in Cologne, they were examined by a psychiatrist who described Masha as being a psychopath. They turned down an offer of separation by a British surgeon, although it is doubtful if separation would have been possible. At fourteen they met a boy called Slava. Dasha appeared to fall in love with him. On being asked to write an essay on the subject of 'My best friend', Slava's effort included the words "Dasha is my best friend. She is clever and studies very diligently in order to get her school diploma and thus be able to work with all other citizens of the Soviet Union to build Communism." They had indeed been indoctrinated into belief in Communism. He also wrote, "… she is kind and thoughtful too. She irons the pinafores of girls who have no arms." This was followed by many more words of praise.

Juliet Butler, a British author, knew them well for fifteen years. In the BBC *Horizon* programme of 2000 she relates, "When Dasha was eighteen she fell in love with a boy called Slava and they were very deeply in love with each other, but Masha had a very different character, being boyish herself. Dasha used to sneak a few kisses but there was no real romance. Masha didn't understand that Dasha was falling in love but, when she realised what was happening, she thought she'd have to put a stop to it. She said to Dasha, 'What are we going to do? You know, I can't live with Slava all my life and I'm certainly, you know, not, happy to have you kissing, I mean, OK, you can turn around and go and kiss but I don't want anything else happening. I mean, I'm not interested in him.' The affair ended; it broke Dasha's heart."

It seems that many of the other children were sexually promiscuous. The twins were curious; they had never had any sex education. When they were sixteen they sought help from the school nurse, asking whether they could have sexual intercourse and whether they could have babies. The reply was blunt: "You can't have sex, you would bleed to death." Nevertheless, on New Year's Eve 1967, when they were aged seventeen and drunk, Slava had intercourse with Dasha. Apparently this was never repeated.

When Dasha was eighteen she became depressed and attempted suicide by hanging. The attempt failed, as the noose slipped off. Soon the twins returned to Moscow, saying goodbye to Slava. Dasha promised to write to him; she was sad. They went to the Twentieth Home for Veterans of War and Labour, Moscow where they remained for twenty years. A few years later the twins learnt that Slava had died. He was nineteen years old; he was the love of Dasha's life, in spite of being only 18 inches tall due to severe kyphosis, scoliosis and poliomyelitis. Subsequently, Dasha attempted suicide at least three more times, but all three attempts failed.

After Mikhail Gorbachev came to power in Russia in 1988, the twins became free to speak out. They appeared on Russian television to great popular acclaim. This resulted in their being given much improved accommodation. Publicity brought aid from the West. They visited Germany. They had two abdominal operations: one was for appendicitis and the other for a twisted bowel (volvulus). In the BBC Television discussion described in the Introduction, they declared their opposition to separation, saying, "We'd never agree to such an operation. We just don't need it. We share our grief and our tears. We're fifty now. We'll stay like this for the rest of our lives." Dasha once said, "If you're sorry for someone it means you think they're worse than you and we don't think we're worse than other people. But we have to keep proving it because of the way we look." They looked for and eventually met their mother and two brothers, who lived in Moscow. Their mother had also looked for the twins' grave, having been told they had died. Failing to find a grave, she visited the Kunst Kamera museum in St Petersburg, which has a large collection of preserved deformed babies. She expected to find her twins in a jar.

The twins had originally sought Juliet Butler in the Moscow office of *Newsweek*. She wrote a biography of the twins in English. It was never published in English, but was translated into German and published in 2000 under the title *Masha und Dasha: Autobiographie eines siamesischen Zwillingspaares*. Butler has also written a novel in English entitled *The Less You Know The Sounder You Sleep*, published in 2017, telling their life story as if told by Dasha. Butler stated, "It's dreadful the things people say to them, it's just appalling, and Masha will always shake her fist at them and scream back at them but Dasha gets very upset and then she'll go home and perhaps cry. One of them said, 'Why are people so nasty to us? Why do they say that we ought to have been killed at birth? Maybe we should have been.'"

In 1991 the twins made their first trip out of Russia when they went to Cologne, where they appeared on television. At the invitation of a French company, they visited Paris on their fiftieth birthday. In 2000 they appeared in the *Guinness Book of Records* as the oldest living conjoined twins.

After many years of struggle against alcohol dependence, Masha died on 17 April 2003 of a heart attack, aged fifty-three. She died in the ambulance on the way to hospital. Dasha was offered separation but refused. She was sedated and died seventeen hours later. They were cremated at their own request so that any further medical investigation would be impossible. Their ashes are interred at Novodevichy Cemetery in Moscow.

Ronnie and Donnie Galyon

Ronnie and Donnie were born on 28 October 1951 in Dayton, Ohio. They are joined from the sternum to the groin (thoracopagus). They share one set of male sex organs. Separation was considered inappropriate.

Their mother rejected them so they were brought up by their father and, later, by their stepmother. They never went to a normal school because of fear of rejection. Their father resolved not to show them but changed his mind when medical bills mounted up and he had nine children to care for. Most of their exhibitions took place in a trailer, with spectators viewing them through a window. By the 1970s such exhibitions had become less acceptable in the USA and so they toured Latin America instead. They have also been interviewed on television.

They have been the subject of harassment, vandalism and threats. However, they have enjoyed retirement since 1991, living with their youngest brother, Jim, and Jim's wife in Ohio in a house bought with their earnings. With help from the local community, it has been enlarged to meet their needs. Jim and his wife help to look after them. They have played baseball with him and have enjoyed fishing. According to a Wikipedia article dated May 2011, they "nearly died last year and now need round-the-clock care".

The Galyons have said that part of the credit for their longevity should go to specialists at Mary Free Bed Rehabilitation Hospital in Grand Rapids, Michigan. The team created a customised bed/chair that gave the twins their first good night's sleep in years.

Celebrations in 2014 began on 5 July, when Ronnie and Donnie Galyon reached a big milestone. They had lived one day longer than their heroes, Chang and Eng Bunker. The Galyons celebrated with a party in Jim and Mary Galyon's home. "It was a really nice turnout," Jim said. They celebrated their sixty-fourth birthday on 28 October 2015 at Disney World and Busch Gardens in Florida.

Napit and Prissana Atkinson

Napit and Prissana were born in Thailand in about 1953. They were probably omphalopagus. Their poor parents consigned the twins to a hospital in Bangkok, where they were discovered by Florence Atkinson in 1953. Eventually Mrs Atkinson arranged for their transfer to Chicago, where they were separated. The twins returned to Thailand, where their parents agreed to the Atkinsons adopting them. This was accomplished, although there were two odd causes of delay. The Thai doctor urged a delay until astrological signs were propitious. Then a Communist member of parliament claimed that the Americans were exploiting the twins but was overruled. They returned to the USA and became American citizens.

The Boko twins (the Conjoined Twins of Kano)

Conjoined twins (both female) were born on 25 July 1953 at Kano, Northern Nigeria. A diagnosis of twins had not been made before birth. One was delivered as a vertex birth (head first) and the other as a breech birth (bottom first). Their combined weight was 7 lbs 13 oz. A student midwife conducted the delivery. The mother was of the Ibo tribe. They were otherwise healthy and were breastfed. A barium meal X-ray of one of them showed that their gastro-intestinal systems were separate. They were transferred to Hammersmith Hospital, London in November 1953. They were called Wariboko and Tomunotonye but are usually referred to as the Boko twins.

They were joined at their abdomens, with a joint umbilicus and fusion of their sternums and three rib cartilages (thoracopagus). There was a connection between their vascular systems, livers and peritoneal cavities. Several investigations were performed, which showed that separation should be possible. Separation was achieved on 3 December 1953. One hour after the operation, Tomunotonye collapsed with a cardiac arrest and died. Her adrenal gland was smaller than normal and was thought to be the cause of the cardiac arrest. Boko recovered and returned to Nigeria with her mother eighteen days after the operation.

Boko celebrated her sixty-second birthday in 2015. She was interviewed on 19 December 2015 by a magazine called *Vanguard*, published on 9 April 2016. The interview included:

I feel very good and thankful to God for keeping me alive all these years. God has been very faithful to me and with me because he has made me fulfill my life till now. All the people I have known are also thankful to God for my life and feel good that they know me. Indeed I thank God so much.

I started to know that I am peculiar from primary school. I think I was in primary one when I started noticing this peculiarity. I was six years old when people won't let me be. They always tell me to lift my dress so they could see the scar on my chest and tummy. At a time, when the disturbance became almost unbearable, I started asking them to pay before I would do that… Beyond that, I discovered that every one treated me differently and with a kind of peculiarity but I was not sure what that was about. Daddy and Mummy, Mr and Mrs Jituboh, were very careful about my diet and about whatever they gave to me… Even at 62, Mr and Mrs Jituboh who raised me still treat me as that same baby I have always been to them since 1953… To them, I am not 62 but still that Wariboko kid whom God gave to them in such circumstances. They have remained very caring parents to me and I won't forget that.

I started to understand my history as life went on… Pressmen and women have always been part of my life. They used to come to the house every now and then. I can't say I asked any questions about my circumstances but started to imbibe them as I grew up.

I learnt that I was born 25 July 1953 to Veronica Davis who was then on staff of the UAC. She had me and my sister conjoined. I also learnt with the photos I have seen that we were separated some time after six months but my sister did not make it.

I also found out that when my grandmother was visiting from Jos, I noticed they discussed about one Veronica and sometimes start to cry. I started to wonder if Mum was dead and that Mrs Jituboh is the mum I know as Mum... I heard that Veronica Davis, my mum, hailed from Delta state. She was working for the UAC when she had me and my late twin sister. She later had another set of twins that died before having another baby who died with her on the same day. You see... my life is a big testimony of God's awesome character. I started at a convent, then Queen Amina in Kaduna which used to be Our Lady of Apostles. I then went to Our Lady's High school before transferring to St Maria Gorretti, Benin. It was excitement all the way. Everyone was fond of me. The Reverend Sister Henrietta continued to treat me like a queen. She always said 'give Wariboko this and that'. Even my grandpa that was father to my father, Mr Jituboh, was the greatest spoiler of me. He would always send me pastries. My interest in nursing had grown while I was at Maria Gorretti and after then, my grandpa, Mr Peter Jituboh, had asked what I wished to be and I told him I have been taken care of by nurses and other hospital people so I wish to also do this. Expecting the result, he died. I was devastated but I felt fulfilled that he had approved my decision to study nursing while his wife, my grandma, carried on. When I passed the school of nursing exam for LUTH and UCH, she boasted with me to her friends about my life. She was there when I had my first baby and she sent me a very beautiful abada wrapper through her daughter, Daddy's younger sister, who brought it to Zaria where we were at the time.

I met him [Lt Walter Oki] after nursing school at LUTH. To be sincere, we met through a relative. He later told me that he had read about me while at the University of Ife and had always asked of me through my relative. Dr Oki was a prominent person known to my family in Benin...

Any time I hear of conjoined twins, I feel like they are just like me and would always want to meet them. While at the school of nursing at LUTH, there were preserved Siamese twins which I did not wish to see because they were already dead. I want to see the ones alive. When I went to ABU, Zaria, a doctor had told me of another set but they had already died. He had said that if I had come earlier that I would have met them alive. So the Sobowales are the first I would see alive. So I was in touch with them until I relocated to the US in the past two years after my retirement from service. Nigeria is not a place where people with my kind of circumstances are appreciated medically like other parts of the world where your peculiar circumstance is a serious issue and are noted and medically attended to. There are health related problems for Siamese twins and in the UK and US they all know and keep checking on you to keep you alive.

Lori and George (Dori, Reba) Schappell

Lori and George, female twins, were called Lori and Dori when born on 18 September 1961 in Reading, Pennsylvania. Later, Dori changed her name to Reba and in 2007 changed it again to George when she/he decided to openly acknowledge that she/he was transgender, having self-identified as male from a young age. Such an event is probably unique among conjoined twins. They are joined at the head (craniopagus). George is shorter and has paraplegia (paralysis from the waist down). As of 2017 they are probably the oldest surviving conjoined twins in the world.

Although neither was intellectually disabled, a court had declared that their parents would be incapable of caring for them. They therefore spent their first twenty-four years at Pennsylvania's Pennhurst State School, a facility for the mentally retarded. Herman and June Sonon looked after them. Lori sold Avon products in the hospital. When grown to adulthood they were able to get the disabled label revoked with the help of Ginny Thornburgh, wife of a former Governor of Pennsylvania, and so were able to go to college.

Lori is able-bodied but George has spina bifida. They use a self-adapted bar stool for locomotion. They live independent lives as far as possible. Since leaving the institution, Lori and George have made successful careers for themselves as individuals.

As a country singer, George has sung in the USA, Germany and Japan. He won the L.A. Music Award for Best New Country Artist in 1997. He sang the song 'Fear of Being Alone' for the film *Stuck On You* (see Chapter 15). Lori insists on paying to attend George's concerts, as she is a fan like the rest of the audience. The twins acted in an episode of the television series *Nip/Tuck*. George has designed support equipment for people with physical handicap. Lori works part-time in a hospital laundry. They live with their pet chihuahua, who is paralysed in the back legs and moves around on a device designed by George. In 2006 George joined the Mormon Church. Lori did not join, but has been supportive of his decision. They appeared in a BBC Television discussion described in the Introduction, where they declared their opposition to separation surgery, saying, "You do not ruin what God has made."

They readily accept publicity and have appeared many times in the media, including in films such as *Face to Face: The Schappell Twins*. "Don't assume [our life] is difficult, until we tell you it is," declared Lori. George said, "There are good days and bad days – so what? This is what we know. We don't hate it, we live it every day. I don't sit around questioning it or asking myself what I could do differently if I were separated." George coined a new word which seems very suitable, '*handicapable*', which means that the handicapped can become capable. Lori also stated, "We never wanted to be separated, we never do want to be separated and our families never ever wanted us separated because we fully believe that God made us this way and He had a purpose for us and you do not ruin what God has made." It is clear that these twins have adapted to their condition to an amazing degree. It would be a deserving tribute to them if the word they coined, handicapable, could become Standard English.

Laleh and Ladan Bijani

Laleh and Ladan were born on 17 January 1974 in Firouzabad, Southern Iran. Their heads were joined (craniopagus). The twins were born into a poor Muslim family of eleven children. The sisters were lost in a hospital in 1979 after the doctors responsible for them had to suddenly leave for the USA during the revolution. The Bijanis' parents did not find the sisters again until several years later in the city of Karaj near Tehran, where Dr Alireza Safaian adopted them. They both graduated in law at Tehran University.

They requested surgery when they were twenty-nine years old. The twins underwent the operation, saying that they knew the risks but wanted to achieve their dream of living independent lives. Ladan wanted to continue as a lawyer; Laleh wanted to become a journalist. They also wanted to look at each other face to face for the first time. Although doctors warned that the surgery could kill one or both of the twins, or leave them brain-dead, they both wished to be separated under all circumstances. Before the final tests ahead of the surgery, Ladan said, "If God wants us to live the rest of our lives as two separate, independent individuals, we will." The decision to operate caused worldwide interest and debate. The operation took place in July 2003 at Raffles Hospital, Singapore. It lasted roughly fifty hours. Although they were successfully separated, they died due to blood loss while under anaesthesia after separation.

Sadly, bitter controversy occurred about who wanted what. Doctors had begged the twins not to go ahead with surgery. Both women insisted, however, that the controversial operation should be carried out. Dr Ben Carson, Director of Paediatric Neurosurgery at Baltimore's Johns Hopkins University Hospital, said he never thought the operation had a reasonable chance of success, and claimed that the team had made "a great deal of effort" to try to talk the twins out of it. However, both the sisters and their family insisted it went ahead. Keith Goh Yu-ching, Associate Professor of Neurosurgery at the Chinese University, was also involved and stated, "But when I look back and ask myself if we could have done things differently, I don't think we could have."

Carson claimed that, after discovering complications during the surgery, he had tried to halt the operation but a relative of the twins vetoed this. From then on, he said, "We all knew that at least one of them would die." The revelation that doctors had tried to halt the operation contradicts claims by the twins' parents, and heightens the controversy that has surrounded the operation. In a newspaper article, their adoptive father, Alireza Safaeian, said that the sisters had tried to block the operation but were ignored by the medical team: "We pleaded with doctors not to operate… but the last time we asked them, they said, 'Sorry, it's already been announced all over the world. We can't cancel.'" The twins' adoptive mother, Iran Karmi, said that Lelah was particularly fearful of the operation and begged her sister to abandon the idea of separation: "She was terrified and crying. But Ladan was adamant." However, Carson, in a US television interview, said that neither twin could be dissuaded from going ahead: "I think even if one minute before surgery, they had said, 'We've changed our minds,' we all would have been extremely happy." Carson added, "a great deal had been learnt from the surgery. What they have contributed to medical science will live far beyond them."

The author's case

After a normal pregnancy, which occurred before the use of ultrasonic scanning, a mother was delivered of her first baby in 1978, a boy weighing 8 lbs. He was fully developed, with a small poorly developed twin attached to the lower abdomen. This was a parasitic twin. A week later the twins were transferred to a specialised surgical unit, where the parasite was removed at the age of two weeks. The surviving twin was found to have three kidneys, two appendixes, a duplicated bowel and bilateral inguinal hernias. All these anomalies were corrected during various subsequent operations. In the absence of scanning it had been impossible to make an antenatal diagnosis. It is common for conjoined twins to have other anomalies.

The problem of only one penis

The following four sets of conjoined twins, all of whom had separation surgery, are considered together because each pair of boys was born with one penis. These four illustrate three different 'solutions' to this problem. The ethical problems involved are discussed in Chapter 12. In two examples, one twin remained male while the other was assigned as female. In another, the single penis was somehow divided to facilitate the survival of two boys. In the fourth example, one boy kept the penis while the other was left as a virtual eunuch.

Lin and Win Htut

Lin and Win, conjoined boys, were born on 18 February 1982 by Caesarean section in Mandalay, Myanmar. They had two heads, four arms and three legs. They shared a liver, urinary tract, pelvis and genitals (thoracopagus). They were sent to Rangoon Children's Hospital in July 1983, where they were spotted by a doctor from the Toronto Hospital for Sick Children. He arranged for them to be transferred to Toronto in 1984 for surgical separation. The considerable costs were shared by the Canadian International Agency and KLM and many of the medical staff waived their fees.

On 28 July 1984 they were separated during a seventeen-hour operation. The vestigial third leg was removed, leaving one leg for each twin. Lin kept the male genitals, while a vagina was constructed from a piece of intestine for Win. Another report I cannot verify stated that they both required colostomies, possibly permanently, and that Lin only received one testicle. Therefore, Win would be brought up as a female and would require female sex hormones. She would obviously not be able to get pregnant. Such a procedure is exceptionally rare. Both were provided with a prosthetic second leg at the Ontario Crippled Children's Center. Objections have been raised to the sexual reassignment at the age of two on the grounds that one testicle could have been given to each twin. It has been claimed that the surgery was therefore essentially experimental and not necessarily in the interests of the twins. Presumably the justification would have been that a reassigned female is more satisfactory than a twin with a testicle and no penis. However, one journalist commented, "Yet to give a forced sex reassignment surgery to a two-year-old is medical barbarity at its very worst."

The twins apparently returned to Toronto on several occasions for physical therapy and to receive prosthetic legs. Although the doctors had always planned for Win to receive female hormones, such treatments were not available in Myanmar. At the age of ten, Win told his mother that he was a boy. The parents complied with their son's wishes and chose to let him live as a male.

Jose and Helena (Joao) Omar
Jose and Joao were born in Mozambique sharing a single penis. They were separated in Portugal in 1999, resulting in Jose being given the penis and Joao being reassigned as female and renamed Helena.

Shiva and Meera (renamed Heera) Ramkhalawan
Shiva and Meera, conjoined boys, were born in 1985 at Chaghunas, Trinidad. Each had two arms and two legs. There was joining of the livers, intestines, urinary tracts and genitals (thoracopagus). When they were nine months old, in October 1985, they were separated during a twenty-two-hour operation at the Hospital for Sick Children in Toronto. The most remarkable feature of the operation involved the separation of the single genitals so that each remained male. Meera, a female name given because the parents thought he

would become female, was renamed Heera, which is a male name. The parents had been concerned that surgeons would be forced to transform one of the boys into a girl, as was done in 1984 during the surgery on the Htut twins that involved many of the same surgeons and other personnel.

Viet and Duc Nguyen

Viet and Duc, conjoined boys, were born in 1981 in the Central Highlands of Vietnam, an area that was heavily sprayed with Agent Orange by the US Army during the war (see Chapter 10). They were joined at the abdomen, with only two legs, one penis, one testicle and a shared anus (omphalopagus). They weighed 5 lbs.

Their mother abandoned them. When less than one year old they were assessed at the Vietnam-East German Friendship Hospital in Hanoi, where a nurse adopted them. The doctors decided against separation as they thought one of them would die.

Professor Fujimoto of Japan took an interest in the twins. He said, "I'll build a wheelchair for Viet and Duc. The chair will contribute to their growth. Above all, our present from over the sea will encourage handicapped people all over the world. It will bind them with friendship, and strengthen worldwide solidarity." More than 21,000 people contributed towards the special chair, which was presented to them in 1985.

The twins were successfully separated on 4 October 1988, when they were seven years old, at Tu Du Maternity Hospital in Ho Chi Minh City. The single penis remained with Duc. The Vietnamese team performed the operation under poor conditions. The country was under embargo after the war, and medical resources were few and far between. Professor Bunro Fujimoto, head of the Negaukai Association, recalled that the operating room did not even have an air conditioner. The situation was also highly risky. If Viet died, his twin would die as well. However, support from Japanese benefactors helped the team succeed.

After the surgery, each of the twins had one leg and Japanese experts provided Duc with an artificial leg. Their family blame Agent Orange, which contained the poison dioxin, for the conjoining. Their mother had farmed in the area where the Americans bombed with this defoliant. Duc recovered from the operation and spent the following years growing up in Peace Village, a special home for the infant victims of Agent Orange/dioxin in the Tu Du hospital. His brother, Viet, suffered from cerebral paralysis caused by a medical condition that occurred before the separation. He died in 2007 aged twenty-six. On hearing of Viet's death, Duc said, "I was shocked when they informed me of his death. I used to wish that my brother would wake up one day despite his desperate condition. Now, I realise that my wish was impossible. I must live my life because of Viet, and try to realise what he could not have. My brother sacrificed parts of his body so that I could live." Duc has done his utmost to overcome his disability and has worked hard to have an independent life. The Japanese provided Duc with a prosthetic leg to make up for the left leg he had lost. After that, he visited Japan many times. He finished senior secondary school and studied computer programming. He became an office worker at the maternity hospital. In 2006, he married Nguyen Thi Thanh Tuyen, whom he had met at a friend's wedding party. On his wedding day, Duc said, "Let us drink a toast to our parents, relatives and individuals who saved my life and who always cared, and to local and foreign organisations that support us. We will give what we get to other Agent Orange victims." Duc and his wife had normal twins in 2009, a boy and girl. The story of Nguyen Duc has inspired Japanese high school teacher Toshiaki Uchimoto to compose a song about peace. The song,

'For a Brighter World', was written after Uchimoto's emotional visit to Vietnam, during which he met Duc and witnessed many of the consequences of the American War. He then spread the song within his school, which Duc visited several times to share his life experiences with Uchimoto's students. "I was extremely moved and dumbstruck when I listened to the song during a dinner in Japan," said Duc, who learnt to speak Japanese in his teens. Wanting Vietnamese people to understand the song, Duc asked singer Nguyen Phi Hung to write Vietnamese lyrics for it. Hung then recorded the song and produced a music video for it. He said, "We decided to produce the music video with truthful and vivid images, expecting anyone watching would be able to understand the message of peace in the song." Duc sought volunteers, including other Agent Orange victims, to act in the video. Uchimoto and Japanese singer Yoshie Ruth Linton, who presented the original Japanese version, also joined Duc and Hung in shooting the video. Thus an inspiring triumph over adversity continues.

In March 2017, at the age of thirty-six, Duc had the chance to meet the Emperor and Empress of Japan during their visit to Vietnam. He was appointed a visiting professor at Hiroshima International University in Hiroshima Prefecture. When he gave a speech in Higashi, Hiroshima City, he told the university of his wish to work in Japan, which has now become a reality.

Judy and Shirley

These twins had a normal delivery on 19 February 1969 in a Vietnamese hospital. The mother was the nineteen-year-old wife of a soldier in the army of South Vietnam (Republic of Vietnam). They were joined at the upper abdomen by a large omphalocele, which is a membranous sac derived from the lining of the abdominal cavity. This contained bowel. Their livers were joined (omphalopagus). They were named after the nurses who initially cared for them. The twins were flown to an American army hospital, where it was decided that they were likely to die if not separated. In spite of the hospital being unsuitable for such surgery, they were successfully separated by US Army doctors. Could this case also be due to the spraying of Agent Orange? (See Chapter 10.)

Ruthie and Verena Cady

Ruthie and Verena were born in 1984 in Durango, Colorado, their conjoined state not being discovered until the birth. They were joined from chest to waist with only one three-chambered heart (thoracopagus). They shared a liver and part of their intestines. It was believed that separation would kill one twin and probably both and so was not attempted. They learnt to walk, dance, ride a special bicycle, swim and roller-skate. Their mother, Marlene, has been quoted as saying, "There are people who come up to us and say, 'Oh, how tragic.' I always tell them the only tragedy is in their interpretation of the girls' situation, because obviously Ruthie and Verena are happy kids. We allow them to explore and they find their own limitations."

When it came to walking, their parents thought that they might take turns at walking forwards or backwards, or that one might dominate the other and always force the other to walk backwards. Instead they learnt to walk sideways, almost like they were dancing.

Their mother was asked if she displayed the twins at fairs. Marlene recalls, "It took me weeks to get over that thoughtless remark. But I was only more convinced of how important it is to share my beautiful girls with the world. I must show people that my daughters emanate love – that it is a blessing to be around them."

As they got older their single malformed heart was unable to pump blood efficiently round their growing bodies. It was Verena who could see what was looming. But, ever the practical one, she planned the funeral for her and her sister, making sure that the guest list was prepared and that her family and friends all knew what was to happen.

They died at the age of seven, Ruthie fifteen minutes ahead of Verena. Mrs Cady said, "Verena talked about the whole thing. She said, 'This is the time we're going to be dying.' She said to go get Daddy, and she gave me a list of friends she wanted to give flowers to. She asked to be cremated because she didn't want to be in a box, she wanted to be free." Their mother commented, "Ruthie and Verena taught us so much, they were a perfect example of sisterhood and unity."

A passing stranger might have assumed that the funeral was a joyous occasion, for the music emanating from Phillips Memorial Baptist Church in Cranston, Rhode Island on that Monday evening was Ruthie and Verena Cady's favourite song. Inside, mothers holding toddlers hummed along with the bouncy 'All I Really Need'.

"Inhale Ruthie and Verena's spirit," the girls' father, Peter Cady, told the hundreds of friends and relatives assembled, "and exhale any sorrow you may feel at their passing."

Patrick and Benjamin Binder

Patrick and Benjamin were born by Caesarean section on 2 February 1987 in Ulm, Germany. When the diagnosis was made before birth their mother seriously considered suicide and killing the twins. However, when the parents first saw them their mother declared, "You are ours and I already love you." The backs of their heads were joined (craniopagus) and they shared some skull bone and some intracranial blood vessels. Their brains were fused and shared the sagittal vein, which is the major vein that drains blood from the brain. The German doctors sought the help of Ben Carson, an American surgeon at Johns Hopkins University Medical Center in Baltimore, Maryland. Carson has described in detail in his book *Gifted Hands* how they proceeded. His description of the twenty-two-hour separation operation is summarised in Chapter 11.

Unfortunately, two years after the separation the twins were both severely brain damaged, and are likely to remain so. The medical bills totalled $300,000, and were paid by West Germany's health insurance scheme.

The *Washington Post* reported that Peter Parlagi, the twins' younger half-brother, said that their father was emotionally unable to ever cope with them. He said the twins' father became an alcoholic, spent all the couple's funds and left their mother destitute and alone. She was forced to institutionalise the twins.

A message that has circulated via email and on social media claims that an attached image depicts conjoined twins separated in an operation conducted by Carson in 1987. The image features a photograph of the conjoined twins before the operation and another supposedly depicting them in more recent times as healthy young adults. This report is a fake and the photos are *not* of the Binder twins.

Abigail and Brittany Hensel

Abigail and Brittany were born on 7 March 1990 in Carver County, Minnesota. They have a single body with separate heads and necks, a chest that is wider than normal, two arms and two legs. They have one spine, two hearts, four lungs, two stomachs, one large intestine, one pelvis, one set of reproductive organs, one bladder and three kidneys (parapagus dicephalus). At birth they had a rudimentary arm attached to a shoulder blade at the back. This arm was removed. Separation was rejected as too drastic as it would have resulted in the death of one twin or survival of both but with one leg each.

Each twin controls her half of their body, operating one of the arms and one of the legs. While each is able to eat and write separately and simultaneously, activities such as running and swimming must be coordinated. Other activities as diverse as hair-brushing and driving a car require that each twin perform a sequence of quite separate actions that coordinate with those of the other twin. By the age of six, they were appearing on the *Oprah* television show in the USA and on the cover of *Life* magazine. At the age of twelve, they underwent surgery at Gillette Children's Specialty Healthcare to correct scoliosis and to expand their chest cavity to prevent future breathing difficulties. Together, they can type on a computer keyboard at a normal speed, drive a car, ride a bicycle and swim. In conversation, the twins are clearly distinct personalities. They have different likes and dislikes; their preferences in food, clothing and colours differ for example. Abby wins some arguments and Brittany wins others. Their friends laugh when they overhear the twins in the background bickering over the choice of a blouse or a pair of shoes. As for their emotional bond, one friend remarks, "They finish each other's sentences, they both know what the other is thinking and what she is going to say. It makes me smile all the time." One of the twins said, "People have been curious about us since we were born, for obvious reasons, but our parents never let us use that as an excuse. We were raised to believe we could do anything we wanted to do." Abby says, "When it comes to decisions, there are compromises we have to make. We take turns, we want to work it so each of us is happy and we find a happy medium." "The most amazing thing about us is we are like everyone else," they chime together. They both graduated from high school in 2008 and then attended Bethel University in St

Paul, Minnesota. They expect to date, get married and have children. Achieving this will obviously present huge problems. For example, as they have only one set of reproductive organs, conception should be possible but who would be the mother? Other problems of marriage by conjoined twins are discussed in Chapter 12. In 2009 Brittany was reported to be engaged. Their mother, Patty Hensel, said she has confidence in the twins' approach to life: "It doesn't matter what the challenges are, they go after it." Abby and Brittany Hensel are close, very close. They may have two separate brains, hearts and sets of lungs, but they share everything else, including, as they say, "a normal life... whatever that is". Abby is the more gregarious and outspoken of the two, according to their large group of friends. But Brittany is more "laid back and chilled" and has a "weird" sense of humour. When Abby drinks caffeinated coffee, Brittany can feel it immediately as her heart races.

Angela and Amy Lakeberg

Angela and Amy were born on 29 June 1993 at Loyola University Medical Center in Chicago by Caesarean section. Their birth raised several significant ethical issues, which are discussed in Chapter 12. They were joined at the chest with only one heart (thoracopagus). Conjoining was diagnosed early during pregnancy. With only one heart, separation would have meant the death of one of them.

Nevertheless, separation was performed on 30 August 1993 at the Children's Hospital of Philadelphia when they were six weeks old. The surgeons had to decide which one would survive. They chose Angela. Pre-operatively, Angela's fingernails were painted pink to make sure she would be salvaged. Angela did survive, the hospital staff providing loving care. The director of the Critical Care Unit stated, "All of us kind of consider ourselves kind of surrogate parents for Angela." She died at ten months of pneumonia aggravated by her deformities. Unfortunately, their mother visited rarely, while their father was in trouble with the law. He was even charged with using funds collected for the twins to binge on alcohol and cocaine.

Shannon and Megan Fanning

Shannon and Megan were born in 1994 at the Lutheran General Hospital, Park Ridge, Illinois. They were joined at the front of their chests and abdomens. Their livers were joined and there was joining of bowel with intestinal obstruction in both twins (thoracopagus). They underwent intensive investigations and care during pregnancy. However, labour threatened at thirty-four weeks and so they were delivered by Caesarean section. Their combined birth weight was 7 lbs 12 oz.

In view of their anomalies they were transferred to the Children's Memorial Medical Center in Park Ridge for an immediate operation. The urgency resulted from the intestinal obstruction. The separation was successful although the twins were at significant risk because of being born prematurely and undergoing major surgery. At the age of one year they were progressing normally.

Their father, Larry Fanning, has written a detailed description of the whole story from before pregnancy up to the twins being healthy at one year of age (*Separated Angels*, 1995). He described their appearance immediately on being born: "Shannon and Megan Fanning entered our world, more or less side by side, arms round one another. They were so beautiful, so perfect." To a greater extent than any other I have come across, this well-written account takes the reader close to the action, as well as providing a sensitive and moving description of the thoughts and emotions of the parents, medical staff and many others involved.

Rosie and Gracie Attard (aka Mary and Jodie in court)
Rosie and Gracie were born on 8 August 2000 by Caesarean section at St Mary's Hospital, Manchester, UK. The parents had travelled from Gozo, a small island near Malta, when conjoined twins were diagnosed. Their pelves were joined, and they had a fused spine and one aorta (ischiopagus). Although they had two hearts, Rosie's was not functioning properly and her brain was very defective. She depended on Gracie's circulatory system. The surgeons advised separation, which would have saved the life of Gracie but sacrificed that of Rosie. Failure to operate would have resulted in the death of both twins before long. The parents refused permission for surgery but were overruled by English courts. Eventually they were separated on 6 November 2000 at St Mary's Hospital in Manchester. Rosie died and was given a big funeral in Malta. Gracie survived but required further surgery to correct other defects. She returned with her parents to Gozo. The ethical and legal issues are described in Chapter 12.

A year later Alan Dickson, one of the surgeons who performed the twenty-hour operation to separate the twins, said, "Gracie is very healthy. She is a sparkling bright infant and a real star at the hospital. She has got over the trauma of such a major operation really well. She is smiling and reaching out for things. She is roaming around on the baby walker with all the other children."

At the age of fourteen, Gracie described her experiences:

"Mum and Dad used to take me to the cemetery where Rosie is buried and tell me: 'She's your sister, and you were twins.' Actually, they said we were joined together. Later I heard them use the word 'conjoined'. I didn't know what it meant, and when I was about seven I got my first dictionary and looked it up. Then I felt confused, but I said to Mum: 'I know what it is now,' although I still didn't really understand. A year or so later, I looked on the internet and found out that our story was a big one that went round the world. I didn't think about that. I just wanted to know exactly what happened. I read the stories and it felt as if I was reading a book about someone else. I didn't exactly feel detached, but I wasn't really involved either. It all happened so long ago, when I was a tiny baby." She also said, "I am not sad because I know she is with the angels. My sister is like my guardian angel. I speak to her when I am nervous and can feel her presence all the time. I know she is smiling down on me."

Gracie Attard with family on Gozo, Malta.

At the age of fourteen Gracie has been described as a livewire. Shrewd, funny and voluble, she loves to cycle and swim. She is determined to become a doctor and has strongly held opinions about most things.

Chapter 7

Twenty-first century

Ahmed and Mohamed Ibrahim

Ahmed and Mohamed were born in 2001 in Egypt. They were joined at the top of their heads (craniopagus). The following year they were taken to the Children's Medical Center in Dallas, Texas. In 2003 they were separated during a thirty-four-hour operation. They received help from the World Craniofacial Foundation and the Ray Tye Medical Foundation. For at least a year they had to wear helmets to protect their brains and skulls. They were able to return to Egypt in 2005. While in the USA they learnt to speak English. Some disability remains but they made a remarkable recovery and were able to attend school. They were growing up normally in 2011.

Vani and Veena

These twins were born on 15 October 2003 in Hyderabad, India. Their heads are joined (cephalopagus). They spent eleven years in hospital and were then transferred to the state-run children's home at Ameerpet. Their parents have abandoned them. On their fourteenth birthday the girls looked cheerful and were showered with goodies and presents. One of the caretakers at the home said that these girls do not need sympathy and are doing well.

There have been efforts since to arrange separation surgery but this has been bedevilled by medical and political confusion. A report in 2017 stated, "The ordeal of the twins started in 2003 and several doctors from across the world were consulted that included Dr Keith Goh, neurosurgeon from East Shore Hospital, Singapore, Dr David Dunaway and Dr Owese Jeelani from London and other doctors too examined the kids but there is a lot of risk and chance of survival is bleak and at least for now, the operation does not seem to happen." Another report stated that, "Two London based doctors have brought new hope into the lives of 11 year old conjoined twins Vani and Veena based at the state run Niloufer hospital by asserting that the success rate to separate the duo is more than 80%. The surgeons said that they were planning to conduct the surgery in five different stages." For some reason, by 2017 this had not taken place.

Lakshmi Tatma
Lakshmi was born in 2005 in Araria district, Bihar, India. She appeared to have four arms and four legs. She was actually one of a pair of ischiopagus conjoined twins, one of which was headless because its head had atrophied and its chest had not fully developed in the womb, causing the appearance of one child with four arms and four legs. This condition can also be called parasitic. Lakshmi's father, Shambhu, and mother, Poonam, were day labourers who earnt less than forty rupees per day and were unable to afford separation surgery for their daughter. She was named after Lakshmi, the Hindu Goddess of Wealth (who is depicted as four-armed). A sacrifice of two

goats reconciled villagers to the family. The mother touched the feet of the villagers as a sign of reconciliation.

Lakshmi was sometimes an object of worship as an incarnation of the goddess; by the age of two, she was known all over India. At one point, a circus offered the couple a sum of money to buy Lakshmi for a sideshow, which forced the family into hiding. At the time of being found by Dr Sharan Patil, Lakshmi was suffering from an infected pressure ulcer at the neck end of the parasitic twin and from continuous fever.

Surgery was performed in Bangalore at the age of two years, when the parasitic twin was removed. Two years later, Lakshmi underwent an operation for club foot and later one for scoliosis. Nine years later she is healthy.

Krishna and Trishna Mollik

Krishna and Trishna were born in December 2006 in Bangladesh. Six weeks later their impoverished parents placed them in the Missionaries of Charity orphanage in the Bangladeshi capital, Dhaka, in the hope that they could receive medical care. The mother is reported to have said that she was blindfolded and had her hands tied when her conjoined babies were born by Caesarean section. She sobbed in disbelief after delivering her daughters, telling *Woman's Day* magazine that she felt "almost dead with shock" when she eventually saw that the girls were joined at the head. "I was so upset to see them in that condition," the twenty-two-year-old said from her home in Bangladesh. "Then the doctors pulled the babies away from me... I was shouting like a crazy person..."

An aid worker, Ms Noble, first saw Trishna and Krishna when they were one month old. The worker contacted the Children First Foundation, which brought the girls to Australia to be operated on. Their heads and brains were joined (craniopagus). They were separated at Melbourne's

Royal Children's Hospital at the age of nearly three years after a long operation. Their mother has spoken of her delight that her children survived the risky operation, but said that she wants them to stay in Australia to have a better life. "I dream my children are safe and happy," she told *Woman's Day*, adding, "I want to talk with my daughters and I'd do anything to see them for just one minute." Apparently they have now been adopted.

Owen and Emett Ezell

Owen and Emett were born on 15 July 2013 in Dallas, Texas. Their parents, Dave and Jenni, already had two sons. The diagnosis was made when Jenni was seventeen weeks pregnant. When Jenni saw the ultrasound scan she immediately recognised conjoined twins. She and her partner seriously considered having an abortion. However, the pregnancy continued, numerous scans showing a joining of the abdomens (omphalopagus). There was a shared liver and spinal deformity together with possible cardiac problems and an omphalocele, which is a hernia with some abdominal organs protruding into the umbilical cord. One of the twins has a missing corpus callosum, which is the structure that joins the two hemispheres of the brain. One twin had palsy of one arm. There were also bowel problems.

Separation took place in 2013. Since then, the twins have required numerous operations and procedures to deal with their other deformities. These have included tracheostomies, stretching of the skin to provide skin grafts, tube-feeding by means of stomach and jejunal tubes and treatment of infections.

Dave and Jenni have written a detailed blog describing these events. They also frequently emphasise the tremendous help they have received from relatives and friends and also their firm reliance on prayer. Many people have provided financial help, including Jenni's brother and his wife, who ran sponsored marathons in Edinburgh. The twins have continued to make progress and seem happy, although their speech development is retarded.

As mentioned in the Introduction, the Ezells run an international support group and are keen to give advice.

Twins of Daniel and Kristin Christensen

In 2018, stillborn conjoined twins were born to Daniel and Kristin Christensen in North Carolina. The parents wished the twins to be cremated. However, a North Carolina state law says two people can't be cremated at the same time. This created a problem for the Christensen family as they did not want burial. The couple said it is medically difficult to tell the two girls apart. Surgical separation was not an option. After unhappy frustration a solution was found. They were cremated in the neighbouring state of Virginia.

Chapter 8

Rare examples and animals

Triplets

Conjoined triplets have been described very rarely, not to be confused with the situation in which conjoined twins occur with another single child.

Triplet boys were born in Italy in 1831. This was a male with three heads on two necks and one trunk. There were three arms, a double upper thorax and two vertebral columns, two tracheas and four lungs. Below the waist the body was single and normal (tricephalus parapagus). During delivery the doctor amputated the first two heads as they appeared in order to facilitate the delivery of the rest of the baby. He was criticised for doing this but replied that there had been no precedent to guide him.

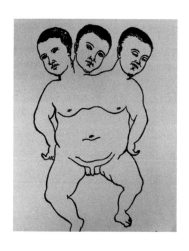

Triple conjoined twins, Italy 1831.

I think he probably had no alternative. A Caesarean section would be performed today but this was unavailable in 1831.

The triplets shown on p.131 were reported in 1897. Two complete bodies were joined near the umbilicus, with a parasitic body attached to the shoulder of one (omphalopagus with rachipagus parasite).

Quadruplets and more

Two examples have been reported. One was in 1870 and the other in 1874. In one there was a relatively normal fetus with a placenta-like mass protruding from the mouth with two fetuses attached, both anencephalic, and with three limbs each. There have been no confirmed reports of conjoined quintuplets or higher. There have been claims of a four-headed child and of six-headed examples but there is no firm evidence to support these claims.

In 1932, stillborn conjoined twins with complicated abnormalities including twelve feet were born in India. Not surprisingly, the local people concluded that this was the incarnation of one of their Hindu deities, which are thought to have several limbs.

Conjoined twins, apparently one male and one female

Born in 1988, these twins appeared to be male and female. This is theoretically impossible because conjoined twins are derived from one fertilised ovum and so must be of the same sex. Probably the explanation is that both twins were female but that one had pseudohermaphroditism, in which the clitoris is abnormally large.

Freemartin syndrome

In 1959, Professor Ian Aird, of Boko twins fame (see Chapter 6), described an example of apparently male twins from

China, one of which seemed eunuchoid in appearance. This would require fusion of twins, one male and the other female, which has never otherwise been observed. Is this nonsense? Probably.

Ectopic conjoined twins

In 1935, conjoined twins were recovered from a ruptured tubal pregnancy. One fetus was 6.5 mm long. They were omphalopagus. In 1986, in the General Hospital of Athens, conjoined twin embryos were found in a tubal pregnancy of about seven weeks' duration. The laterally united twins (parapagus) were about 2 cm long, having two heads, two upper limbs and four lower limbs. The gastro-intestinal tract was double and the heart and liver were single. This was thought to be the only example ever described, but probably the authors had not noticed the 1935 case, which was reported in a German journal. These two reports are probably the only examples of ectopic conjoined twins ever reported.

Joined in two places

Two examples have been described of conjoined twins joined at two separate places. In 1906, an aborted embryo, 8 mm long, had joining at the head and chest. In 1922, a similar example occurred in a fetus spontaneously aborted at six months. The extreme rarity of this phenomenon makes it very unlikely that the Biddenden twins (see Chapter 1) were joined in two places, as their traditional representation suggests.

Two examples in the same family – the Libbera family

I have only found one example of two cases in the same family. Jean Libbera, described in Chapter 4, was born in 1884 in Rome. He had a parasitic twin called Jacques attached to his chest. He had twelve siblings, of which he was the fourth. It is claimed that the third had a similar condition but did not survive.

Prenatal death of one conjoined twin
In 1990, in the USA, one of a pair of conjoined fetuses died at about fourteen weeks, while the other continued to live and survived childhood. During pregnancy, the deceased twin became squashed flat to become what is known as a fetus papyraceous.

A bizarre case
In 1924, a man requested removal of some tissue near his ear. He claimed that this was the site of an attached conjoined female twin who had died at the age of six years. The conjoined twin could not have been female. The report is so bizarre that I suspect it was fictional.

Conjoined twins after ICSI
Intracytoplasmic sperm injection (ICSI) is the injection of a single sperm into an ovum. This can be performed for some cases of infertility.

1. **An omphalopagus parasitic twin**
    In 2004, a thirty-year-old pregnant Japanese woman with a history of secondary infertility was reported to have conceived after ICSI. An omphalopagus parasitic twin pregnancy was diagnosed by prenatal ultrasound at twenty-eight weeks of gestation. Delivery was by Caesarean section at thirty weeks of gestation. Resuscitation was not attempted because of the poor prognosis for both fetuses. Molecular analysis with informative genetic markers was consistent with monozygotic pregnancy, indicating that the pregnancy

resulted from one sperm and one ovum. Therefore, the twins must have occurred by division of the fertilised ovum and not by fusion (see Chapter 10).

2.   **Therapeutic abortion**

In 2010, a case of conjoined twins in a thirty-year-old woman following ICSI was reported. The diagnosis of conjoined twins was made by vaginal ultrasonography after nine weeks of gestation. The conjoined fetuses were diagnosed as thoracopagus twins with a single beating heart shared between the thoraxes. Extensive ultrasound examination suggested an extremely poor prognosis. Therapeutic termination was performed at eleven weeks.

Fetus in fetu

This is a deformed fetus enclosed within a normal person. Therefore, it is not strictly an example of conjoined twins but is worth describing here if only because the media have been known to use the term 'conjoined twins' in such cases.

The condition is very rare. Such a fetus is almost certainly a monozygotic twin of the host person. It may be situated in various parts of the body. There have been examples in the abdomen, thorax, gonads and intracranial region. Fanciful descriptions have been made, such as that this is a repetition of the process by which Eve was born of Adam or that a man may be pregnant with his sister, both of which are impossible.

A very rare example occurred in 2000 in Texas, when a newborn boy was found to have a fetus in his abdomen. This was a fetus in fetu which had developed to eighteen-week size. It was removed seven days after the birth. The boy also had several congenital abnormalities requiring several operations, including liver and bowel transplants.

Animals

Conjoined twins occur in the animal kingdom. Some authorities claim that conjoined twinning in animals is more common than in humans, whilst others claim it is less common. As there is no notification or registration of any kind for such animals it is impossible to know the true frequency.

The earliest example must be that of the fossilised remains of a young *Hyphalosaurus lingyuanensis*, a two-headed marine reptile that lived 150 million years ago. It was found in north-eastern China by Jianjun Li and Eric Buffetaut. It was about 8 cm long; an adult would be about 90 cm long.

Most conjoined animals probably do not survive for long. However, in 1894 a two-headed partridge in Boston, Massachusetts was reported to have lived to adulthood.

There is a museum of conjoined animals within the Venice Beach Freak Show in Los Angeles, where there are reputed to be twenty live examples. They claim this to be the world's largest collection, including a cow, chicken, racoon, iguana, turtles and other animals. Many museums round the world have examples. Many are listed in the Wikipedia article 'Polycephaly'.

A two-headed albino rat-snake called We was born in 2000. An attempt was made to auction it on eBay for an expected $150,000 but was refused because eBay will not trade in live animals. We was acquired by the Nutra Pharma Corporation and died naturally at the age of eight.

At least six examples are preserved in UK museums:
- Hereford: a two-headed calf
- Eton College, Windsor: a four-footed duckling and a two-headed kitten
- Llanidloes, Powys, Wales: a two-headed lamb

Two-headed calf, Hereford. UK.
Reproduced by permission Hereford
Museum and Art Gallery.
~~Eton College~~.

Four-legged chick. Reproduced by
permission pf Provost and Fellows of
Eton College.

Two-headed cat. Reproduced by
permission of Provost and Fellows of
Eton College.

Two-headed Lamb. Permission
Llandloes Museum, Powysland
Museum and Welshpool Library.

The calves at Mowbray were born at Braunston, Rutland, around 1900. They were delivered by Justus Littler, an Oakham vet, but lived only a few hours. Mr Littler preserved them and they were displayed for many years in the Littler veterinary practice in Melton. During both World Wars they were regularly displayed in peep shows in the cattle market to raise money for the Red Cross and other charities. In the late 1970s the veterinary practice closed and the calves were presented to the Melton Carnegie Museum.

Conjoined calves were born in 2011 at Pascoe, Florida. What happened was described in the *Tri-City Herald*:

Martin Cervantes an experienced farmer wasn't prepared for what he saw when one of his family's ewes gave birth. The ewe gave birth to conjoined twin lambs. Neither lamb survived long. "He was surprised," said his daughter, Nayeli. "He called his veterinarian, who said it would be very expensive to separate them."

Although the birth was something new for Martin, Charlie Powell, spokesman for the Washington State University College of Veterinary Medicine in Pullman, said the university has several mounted sets that veterinary and pathology students study so they can learn more about such occurrences.

Martin Cervantes, however, has a theory on what happened to the lambs. He saw animals without tails and without feet during an eclipse. He said people believed that was because the animals' mothers were pregnant during an eclipse. As prevention against such birth defects, he said, it was a Mexican custom to tie a red ribbon around the tail of a cow whose pregnancy occurred during an eclipse. Nayeli said her family didn't follow that custom here, though, "because they haven't had any problems during an eclipse". She has her own opinion on the family's experience: "It's kind of cool, but it's really weird."

A hoax?

A picture of apparently conjoined pikes has been circulating on the internet since at least 2001. Whether they are genuine or not has been debated. Doubt arises because several states in the USA have claimed to be the site of discovery. One suggestion is that one fish forced its way through the gill plate into the mouth of the other, either spontaneously or by a hoaxer.

Pubs

There are at least three pubs in Britain called The Swan With Two Necks or a similar title. They are at Pendleton near Clitheroe, Blackbrook in Staffordshire and Great Yarmouth. There also used to be one in Norwich marketplace but it closed in 1898.

Shakespeare

Could it be that the bard had seen conjoined fishes hanging up in a rundown shop such as that described in his play *Romeo and Juliet?*

Suicidal Romeo is seeking to buy poison and finds a shop:

And in this needy shop a tortoise hung,
An alligator stuffed, and other skins
Of ill-shaped fishes…

Romeo and Juliet, Act V Scene I

Animals in fiction
Many-headed beasts have made plenty of appearances in modern-day fiction, from *Fluffy* the huge three-headed dog in *Harry Potter and the Philosopher's Stone* to *Sesame Street*'s bungling two-headed monster.

Chapter 9

Types, frequency and causes of multiple pregnancy

Types of twins

Before we consider the frequency and possible causes of conjoined twins it will be helpful to look at the types, frequency and causes of multiple pregnancy in general.

Human cells have twenty-three pairs of chromosomes in their nuclei, making a total of forty-six. Ova and sperms are haploid gametes each having twenty-three unpaired chromosomes. A diploid cell results from the fusion of one ovum and one sperm, i.e. two haploid gametes, resulting in a fertilised ovum, which has forty-six chromosomes. This is called a zygote. Twins may be either monozygous or dizygous.

Monozygous twins (MZ): The fertilised ovum is derived from one zygote. This divides so that each twin has the same genetic make-up; therefore, they must be similar to each other in appearance and be of the same sex. They are usually called 'identical twins'. However, they may have noticeable differences, especially in their personalities.

If the separation occurs during the first three days after fertilisation, the twins are separated by two layers of membrane: the amnion, which is touching the fetus, and the chorion, which encloses the amnion. If the separation occurs later then they may be separated only by the amnion. Rarely, in about 1% of cases, a membrane does not separate them, so that the twins are touching each other. In this case, there is a considerable danger of their umbilical cords becoming tangled during the pregnancy, resulting in the death of one or both twins and leading to either miscarriage or stillbirth.

Monozygous twins may have one placenta, in which case there may be a communication within the placenta between the blood vessels of each twin. In this case, the more robust twin may take blood from the weaker one, resulting in it being born congested with too much blood while the weaker one is born anaemic with too little blood. As a result, one or both twins may die. This can also happen with conjoined twins.

Dizygous twins (DZ): There are two ova fertilised by two sperms. There are two complete sets of membranes and two placentas, although the placentae may fuse together. The blood vessels of the twins within the placenta do not communicate. The twins may be of the same or different sexes and will only resemble each other to the same extent that any siblings resemble each other. They cannot become conjoined. The fertilisation normally results from one act of sexual intercourse. With multiple births in which there are triplets or more, the individuals may be any combination of monozygous and dizygous types.

Diagnosis of zygosity: It is important to diagnose this if possible. If the twins are of different sexes they must be dizygous. If they are of the same sex then they could be of either kind. If a same-sex pair has a placenta with one chorion then they are monozygous. If there are two chorions they could be of either type. The most accurate diagnosis is made by DNA testing.

Causes of multiple pregnancy

How have you made division of yourself?

Antonio to Sebastian, *Twelfth Night*, Act V Scene I

Monozygotic multiple pregnancy

The cause is not known but probably involves chromosomal anomalies, especially X-linked ones. Mutations may also be relevant. About 10–15% of MZ twins have congenital abnormalities, a rate much higher than in single individuals. It has been suggested that delayed implantation of the fertilised ovum predisposes to MZ multiple pregnancy. MZ twins are probably not genetic, that is, not inherited, and therefore unlikely to occur again in the same family.

Dizygotic multiple pregnancy

Ovaries contain a large number of primordial (primitive) follicles. During each monthly cycle one or more develop into mature follicles (eggs) capable of being fertilised. This development occurs under the influence of follicle-stimulating hormone, which is produced by the pituitary gland in the brain. DZ pregnancy occurs when more than one follicle matures and are fertilised.

Age: DZ pregnancy is more likely to occur as women get older, with the maximum frequency occurring at about 35–39 years of age.

Increasing parity: An increasing number of previous pregnancies predisposes to DZ twins.

143

Nutrition: It has been claimed that improved nutrition increases the likelihood of DZ twinning. However, many years ago, in Nigeria, I found some evidence that poorer women seemed to give birth to a higher proportion of DZ twins, possibly due to malnutrition. If this is so it could help to explain why the frequency of twinning is so high in parts of Africa and other Third World countries.

Assisted reproduction: In-vitro fertilisation procedures (so called test-tube conception) usually induce the production of several mature follicles. This results in more DZ conceptions. However, more recently, measures have been taken to restrict the number of mature follicles produced to one or two and also to implant into the uterus only one or two fertilised eggs, in order to discourage multiple pregnancy.

Inheritance: There is a tendency for women whose maternal ancestors had DZ twins to have a higher-than-normal chance of having DZ twins.

Superfecundation: DZ twins could result from two acts of intercourse during the same menstrual cycle; this could even involve two different men! DNA testing may be necessary to sort out what has happened.

Although all these factors are relevant, essentially it remains a mystery why some women produce twins. After all, it is only a minority of those in the predisposed groups who actually bear twins.

Frequency of multiple births, including conjoined twins

MZ twins occur randomly, at a rate of about one in 250 pregnancies, and this rate is fairly constant worldwide. The DZ rate varies widely worldwide but is about 12/1000 pregnancies in the UK.

Note that these rates are per pregnancy. Thus the frequency of twins in the population is likely to be twice the frequency quoted. Actually, to be more accurate, nearly twice, because a higher proportion of twins than single babies are stillborn or die in infancy.

Ethnicity: There are considerable variations in the frequency of DZ twins in different ethnic groups. Rates in Africa are high, about one in eighteen to sixty. For example, in the Ibo tribe of Nigeria, the rate is about one in twenty-nine. The Yorubas of Nigeria have a rate of about one in eighteen, which may be the highest in the world.

Rates in Japan and Asia are low, about one in 300 pregnancies. Afro-Americans seem to be intermediate between those for North American whites and Africans. Could this be due to racial mixing of their slave-derived population? In whites, it is about one in sixty to one hundred pregnancies, one in sixty-four in the UK in 2012.

These differences are due to variations in dizygous rates, as monozygous rates, as observed above, are fairly constant worldwide. Approximately two-thirds of twins are dizygotic.

Since 1970, the prevalence of multiple births has been increasing in Britain, the USA and other countries. A combination of factors is responsible, including the increased use of artificial conception and increasing maternal age at birth.

Frequency of conjoined twins: Only about three sets of conjoined twins are born alive in England and Wales each year. About six sets are stillborn and about three-quarters are legally aborted, having been diagnosed in early pregnancy. The number of legal abortions has increased due to improved methods of early antenatal diagnosis (see Chapter 11). There must also be an unknown number that abort spontaneously (miscarriages). The female:male ratio is 3:1. The reason for this is not known.

The frequency of conjoined twins conceived is thought to be about one pair in 50,000–100,000 pregnancies, many of which are aborted spontaneously or medically aborted either legally or illegally. As the frequency of monozygous twins is fairly constant throughout the world, one would expect the frequency of conjoined twins to also be constant. The varying accuracy of vital statistics around the world makes this difficult to confirm. However, one report estimates the frequency in China to be one in 33,000. Unknown environmental or genetic factors could be responsible for variations.

In the UK, accurate data on conjoined twins are kept by the British Congenital Anomaly Registers, which cover about 36% of the population of England and Wales*. Data for the rest of the country are less accurate. These show that, during the years 2005–2009, there were three live births, six fetal deaths** and thirty-one medical (legal) terminations of pregnancy among conjoined twins. During that time there were 1,225,279 births. Therefore, the frequency of conjoined twins was about one in 30,000, or 3.3 in 100,000. This is remarkably similar to the rates for the USA and China.

If the data for 36% of the population during a four-year period are representative, it may be concluded that, in England and Wales, conjoined twins result in about two or three live births, three or four fetal deaths and seventeen legal terminations of pregnancies each year. It can also be seen that, in the UK, about three-quarters of cases are legally aborted, having been diagnosed in early pregnancy.

*East Midlands, South Yorkshire, Northern England and South West England.

**Fetal death refers to born dead after twenty weeks of gestation; this includes stillbirth. Stillbirth refers to born dead after twenty-four weeks.

Chapter 10

Causes and mechanism of conjoining

Causes of conjoined twinning

Traditional theories

In spite of phenomenal advances in science we are still in the dark about the causes of conjoining. It is interesting, however, to reflect on the many unscientific explanations which have surfaced through the ages, and also on some possible environmental factors.

Early ideas

North American myths include the idea that all twins are united in the uterus but forced apart at birth, or that twins in the uterus fuse to make one fetus. The latter myth is personified in the autobiography of Hopi Don Talayesva. Before birth, Hopi had been twins but his mother desired one child so, with the help of a medicine man, she willed the fusion. Hopi believed that his newborn appearance confirmed these facts. His hair had two whorls. The front of his body was male but, at the back, there was the trace of a girl, namely the imprint of a vulva. It is possible that the so-called vulva was actually a small spina bifida deformity.

A Lakota shaman, of the North American Sioux tribe, is reputed to have said or written, "They [twins] are not like other men, but the Great Spirit made them *winktes* [male transsexuals] and we accepted them as such… We think that if a woman has two little ones growing inside her, if she is going to have twins, sometimes instead of giving birth to two babies they have formed up in her womb into just one…"

Imagination

This superstitious explanation has been around from ancient times up to at least until the nineteenth century. The idea is that events occurring to the mother during pregnancy can have a harmful psychosomatic effect on the fetus. A simple example is that of two women near Worms, Germany, in 1495, who accidentally bumped their heads, this being blamed for the subsequent delivery by one of the women of conjoined twins.

Even animals are claimed to be susceptible. Advocates claim biblical support. In the book of Genesis (30.37–43), Jacob placed striped branches before mating goats, which caused their young to be streaked. He later placed the branches before the strong animals, who bred more strong animals, leaving the weakest for Laban. This is an example of genetic breeding!

Ambroise Paré (1510–1590) gives the power of the imagination as one of thirteen possible causes of anomalies including conjoined twins. The others appear below. The Bunker twins were at first refused entry to France because the authorities were afraid that French pregnant women would be affected, resulting in more conjoined twins. A few years later the authorities changed their minds and the twins were allowed entry.

In 1726 Mary Toft, of London, claimed to have given birth to sixteen rabbits and a tabby cat over the course of months, attributing this to having been startled by a rabbit while a child, followed by her desire to eat the rabbit, a wish that was not fulfilled. She later confessed to fraud. This was soon followed by a serious, well-publicised debate between Daniel Turner, who believed the imagination theory, and James Blondel, who did not. Both were members of the London College of Physicians. The debate was conducted through pamphlets.

Philip Wilson has given a detailed account of the pamphlet debate. Blondel claimed, rightly, that maternal and fetal blood do not mix. Therefore, how could one influence the other? Turner pointed out the well-accepted influence of the mind on the body. He also referred to many historical examples of claims of antenatal events causing deformities, quoting Aristotle, Pliny, Soranus, Paré, Bartholin and Robert Boyle, among others. How does one prove those authorities to be mistaken? Today we know that Blondel was right but the debate shows how extraordinarily difficult it was, and is, to actually prove the imagination theory to be wrong. Blondel argued that, if impressions are so potent, there should be far more abnormal babies than there are, the mystery being not why anomalies occur but why they are so uncommon.

It is the impossibility of proving that impressions are a cause, together with the philosophy of science, which convinces us today that impression theory is wrong.

Divine intervention
In the Bible, Jesus explains to his disciples (John 9.1–3) that a certain man is blind so that God's power might be seen at work. Modern Christians are unlikely to endorse this view, although Ambroise Paré agrees that blindness is an example of the glory of God. He then gives the wrath of God as another

of his thirteen possible causes. He refers to the Apocrypha, in which the prophet Edras claims that, one day, "Women shall bring forth monsters." Paré elaborates, "It is certain that most often these monstrous and marvellous creatures proceed from the judgement of God, who permits fathers and mothers to produce such abominations from the disorder that they make in copulation, like brutish beasts, in which appetite guides them." He further claims that intercourse during menstruation can cause all manner of diseases.

A sixteenth-century ballad said, "The monstrous and unnatural shapes of these children are evidence that God is offended with the parents for some notorious vice or offence." Witchcraft was also blamed.

It has been alleged that Catholic literature used monsters as polemics against the Protestants. Protestant ballads associated monsters with evil behaviour, provoking God's anger. Thomas Bedford, an English cleric, wrote in 1632, "They [monsters] are shewed that they may shew the special handyworke of God, and though, peradventure dead, yet speake and tell the worlde, that God himself hath a speciall hand in forming and featuring the births conceived in the wombe."

Du Verney described conjoined twin boys born in 1706 near Paris. He persuaded some people that they make us aware of the richness of their creator's mechanical knowledge and resources and the flexibility with which these are deployed and displayed. Michel de Montaigne (1533–1592), on seeing a set of conjoined twins, declared, "Those which we call monsters are not so with God, who in the immensitie of his work seeth the infinite of formes therin contained… From out his all-seeing wisdome proceedeth noting but good."

God or accident? Philip Wilson summed up: "The main controversy raised… is the disagreement between those who declare that the monster is already there in the egg (and therefore was put there by God or a similar power) and those who declare that it is due to an accident, such as the squashing together of two eggs in the womb producing, not ordinary twins, but conjoined twins."

Paré's thirteen

Ambroise Paré, born in France, was chief surgeon to Charles IX and Henri III. He is famous for having discovered that the amputated stumps of injured soldiers healed better if treated with a mixture of egg yolk, rose oil and turpentine, rather than with boiling oil.

In his book *Monsters and Marvels* he speculates about what he calls human and animal monsters and provides many drawings of conjoined twins and part-human, part-animal monsters. Most are clearly the product of his imagination. However, he seriously suggests thirteen possible causes, three of which have been mentioned above, namely imagination, glory of God and wrath of God. The rest are: too much seed, too little seed, narrowness or smallness of the womb, indecent posture of the mother as when sitting with legs crossed during pregnancy, abdominal injury, hereditary or accidental illness, rotten seed, mixture of seed [what does this mean?], 'artifice of wicked spital beggars' and via the agency of demons and devils.

Animalcula

William Smellie (1697–1763) was one of Britain's most famous obstetricians. His book *A Treatise on the Theory and Practice of Midwifery*, published in 1752, includes the following statement: "When two children are distinct, they are called twins; and monsters when they are joined together; the first… are produced when different *Animalcula* impregnate different *Ova*; and the last are engendered when two or more

Animalcula introduce themselves, and are included in one *ovum*". An animalcule refers to a small creature. He thus anticipated the concept of sperms.

Preformation

This is a philosophical theory of heredity, claiming that either the egg or the sperm (exactly which was a contentious issue) contained a complete preformed individual called a homunculus. Development was therefore a matter of enlarging this into a fully formed being.

The term homunculus was later used in the discussion of conception and birth. Nicolaas Hartsoeker (1656–1683) of the Netherlands claimed to have discovered animalcula in the semen of humans and other animals. This was the beginning of the spermists' theory, which held the belief that the sperm was in fact a 'little man' (homunculus) that was placed inside a woman for growth into a child. This seemed to them to neatly explain many of the mysteries of conception. It was later pointed out that, if the sperm was a homunculus, identical in all but size to an adult, then the homunculus might have sperm of its own. This led to a *reductio ad absurdum*, with a chain of homunculi *ad infinitum*. This was not necessarily considered by spermists to be a fatal objection, however, as it neatly explained how it was that, in Adam, all had sinned: the whole of humanity was already contained in his loins. However, the spermists' theory also failed to explain why children tend to resemble their mothers as well as their fathers, although some spermists believed that the growing homunculus assimilated maternal characteristics from the womb environment in which it grew.

Reincarnation

Conjoined twins with two heads born in Nalla, Sopara, India in 1999 were considered by their parents to be a reincarnation of the Hindu deity Vishnu. I do not know whether this was considered an honour or a punishment. The Hindu belief that everyone is reincarnated in a form that reflects the good or bad in one's former life could well be seen by them as an explanation for conjoined twins. I knew of one young Indian lady who bitterly blamed her previous life for her absent uterus and vagina, declaring, "I must have been like Hitler."

A terrible sense of guilt must have been added to her physical problem.

Astrology
Leslie Fiedler has discussed the possibility of astrological explanations. Some believe that there are astrological associations with human disease. It has been suggested that the star Formalheut is involved with congenital birth defects. This is of course unscientific.

Modern theories
Whatever causes we may deduce, they must be related to the causation of monozygous multiple pregnancy itself.

Epidemics

The occurrence of a cluster of cases could indicate some environmental factor at work, or some genetic factor. No such factors could be found in any of the following five epidemics. The clusters could have been due to chance.

Cardiff, UK
There were four sets in fourteen months in a hospital with 2800 deliveries per year.

Zimbabwe

Six sets occurred in a small area of Zimbabwe with a population of 500,000 between 1975 and 1981. All were black and of the Shona tribe. During this time, only two other sets occurred in the whole of the rest of Zimbabwe.

Sweden

Three sets were born at the Skovde Central Hospital in Sweden between 1975 and 1976. During that time there were approximately 6900 deliveries at that hospital, giving an incidence of one in 2300. The incidence for Sweden as a whole was about one in 75,000 births.

New York State

There were six sets in New York State in 1959 and thirteen between 1957 and 1960 in a population of about five and a half million.

Jerusalem

Between January 1976 and December 1981 there were ten sets of conjoined twins, all of them thorapagus. This was an incidence of one in 10,000 births, whereas the incidence for the whole of Israel during that time was one in 475,000 births.

Radiation

Atomic weapons

There was a fear that the children of women who survived the atomic bomb attacks on Hiroshima and Nagasaki in Japan in 1945 would be at increased risk of birth defects. There were some reports claiming increases in mental defects and neonatal and infant deaths. However, the United Nations

Scientific Committee on the Effects of Atomic Radiation found no significant increase in birth defects, except for an increase in microcephaly during a six-year follow-up of nearly all pregnancies in Hiroshima and Nagasaki beginning in 1948. Subsequent study, years later, has confirmed this conclusion. These reports did not report any increase in the frequency of conjoined twins.

Radioactive waste, St Louis County, Missouri

In 2011, in St Louis County, Janell Wright and several of her class of 1988 of McCluer North High School started wondering why so many of their former classmates had been diagnosed with cancer, and had given birth to children with an unexpectedly high frequency of birth defects. They began investigating and found that the neighbourhood affected was Cold Water Creek and the West Lake landfill site. The birth defects included three examples of conjoined twins occurring within an area of four square miles. One report used the words, "The data includes multiple incidents of conjoined twins."

It then became known that, in the 1940s, Mallinckrodt Chemical Works in downtown St Louis, working for the Manhattan Project/Atomic Energy Commission, had purified thousands of tons of uranium to make the first atomic bombs. This process produced radioactive waste, which was moved to north St Louis County. Twenty-one acres of airport land became a dumping site for a toxic mixture of uranium-235, radon, polonium, thorium, thallium and radium.

In the 1960s, government documents noted that contents from the rusting barrels were seeping into nearby Cold Water Creek. And by the 1990s, the government confirmed unsafe levels of radioactive materials in the water. Mallinckrodt Works have denied involvement in the disposal or clean-up of the nuclear waste. In recent years, environmental remediation has been proceeding. Litigation has had varying results. As is usual in such a situation, it is impossible to prove that any individual anomaly, including the alleged three sets of conjoined twins, were caused by radiation, as they could also have occurred by chance.

Chernobyl nuclear reactor explosion

Radiation from the Chernobyl nuclear reactor explosion in 1986 has caused considerable biological damage. With regard to congenital abnormalities, the main effect noticed has been an increase in the incidence of neural tube defects, namely anencephaly and spina bifida. The most severe radiation affected the north-west of Ukraine. One part of this area is the Rivne Oblast district. Between 2000 and 2007, six sets of conjoined twins were born there. One twin in this series had spina bifida. The incidence of conjoined twins (one in 16,381 births) is much higher than would be expected. Surrounding districts did not report additional cases. The incidence of conjoined twins in Rivne was 0.62 per million, compared with 0.18 for Europe. However, the United Nations Scientific Committee on the Effects of Atomic Radiation (2008), reporting on the effects of the Chernobyl disaster, did not find any unexpected increase in conjoined twins in either humans or animals, although there were increases in other anomalies, such as neural tube defects (spina bifida). The UN report strangely contradicts the Rivne Oblast report.

Health News reported on 24 March 2010 that the journal *Pediatrics* reported that Rivne also appeared to have elevated rates of conjoined twins – 0.6%, compared with the roughly 0.2% average estimated for Europe. This data is very similar to that quoted above and may refer to the same original study.

With regard to animals, I have not found any published reports. However, school children from Chernobyl, visiting the museum at Melton Mowbray, Leicestershire, England in July 2012, on seeing the preserved double cow in that museum, were reported to me as declaring that they had seen several conjoined animals back home.

Some reports now claim that internal irradiation, i.e. as a result of ingestion and inhalation, can affect the female reproductive system, causing birth abnormalities. These effects are passed on to the next generation. As a result, it is claimed, women exposed as children to the Chernobyl radiation now have an increased risk of malformed babies.

Therefore, one may conclude that some of the evidence is highly suggestive that the Chernobyl disaster caused some cases of conjoined twins.

The Iraqi wars: Fallujah and Basra

The Iraqi wars took place between 2003 and 2011, although fighting continued after that. There have been numerous reports of increased numbers of birth defects since heavy bombing took place. The areas most affected have been Fallujah and Basra. There have been reports of the birth of conjoined twins, although no numbers are available. For example, Al Jazeera reported, "children being born with two heads, children born with only one eye, multiple tumours, disfiguring facial and body deformities, and complex nervous system problems". The suggested cause is the intensive use by the USA and Britain of bombs using depleted uranium (DU), which is a heavy metal produced in nuclear waste.

DU has a lower content of the fissile isotope uranium-235 than natural uranium. It is a chemically toxic heavy metal produced in nuclear waste, and is used in weapons due to its ability to pierce armour. This is why the USA and UK were among a handful of nations, along with France and Israel, who refused to sign an international agreement to limit its use, insisting that DU is not harmful, science be damned!

Some authorities, such as the Iraqi Ministry of Health, have denied that DU is a problem. The Ministry's report has been strongly criticised by doctors and others, who claim they were not consulted by the Ministry during its investigation. Photographs of deformed children, including conjoined twins, are available on the internet, although a few photographs do not constitute proof. The World Health Organization states that no reproductive, developmental or carcinogenic effects have been reported in humans due to DU exposure. Whether conjoined twins have been caused must remain uncertain.

Nuclear reactor disaster at Fukushima, Japan

The Fukushima nuclear reactor disaster was caused by an earthquake in March 2011. There has been one suspected case of conjoined twins so far, which were possibly conceived about April 2011 in the contaminated region. However, one example proves nothing.

It is surprising that radiation from atomic bombs seems to have had no effect on birth defects except for a possible increase in microcephaly, whereas radiation leaks in some of the examples described above may have done so. Why is this? It has been suggested that studies, such as the decades-long Hiroshima survivors' study, focused on external radiation, i.e. exposure to radiation that passes through the body. In contrast, in the areas affected by Chernobyl, internal emitters are the cause of health effects. This means that radionuclides (alpha and beta particles) in soil and water enter the body, are breathed in or ingested and, after lodging inside the body, continue to irradiate body cells.

Defoliation in Vietnam

Between 1961 and 1971, 46 million litres of Agent Orange and other chemical agents were sprayed over southern and central Vietnam by the USA in an operation called Operation Ranchhand. The object was to defoliate the landscape to prevent the Viet Cong soldiers from hiding and to destroy their food supply. Agent Orange contains dioxin, which is the deadliest poison known to have caused birth defects in rats and mice. Its toxicity was increased by burning. Five million people in 20,000 villages were affected. It has been claimed that this caused many abortions, birth defects, conjoined twins, cancer and other illnesses. This possible danger was debated by the Americans during the war.

Dr Le Cao Dai, a leading Vietnamese expert on birth defects, states that three provinces outside Ho Chi Minh City reported thirty pairs of conjoined twins in just five years. Under normal circumstances, says Dr Dai, the entire country could expect only one set in ten years. Even clothes designed for conjoined twins were marketed, suggesting that there were several examples. Blood tests show that levels of dioxin in southern Vietnamese women are high compared with their counterparts in the north, where there was no spraying. These women are alleged to have ten times as many miscarriages and twice as many abnormal births as those in the north.

Dinh Q. Le, in a book called *Damaged Gene*, which is now unobtainable, claims that there were a large number of conjoined twins resulting from the use of defoliants. He even opened a market stall to sell clothes he had designed for such twins.

Anthony Spaeth, in an article entitled 'Children of Apocalypse', claimed that the children's health centre in Song Be province contains preserved specimens of conjoined twins and that, "nearly every maternity hospital in Vietnam has a similar museum of horrors".

When interviewed by Peter Korn in *The Nation* (issue dated 8 April 1991), Dr Nguyen Thi Ngoc Phuong of the Tu Du Maternity Hospital in Vietnam stated, "And there is… an inexplicable anomaly that has confounded Vietnamese physicians. As many as ten pairs of Siamese twins have been born here each year, when one case every ten to fifteen years would be expected."

Only one set of conjoined twins has had much publicity, namely the Nguyen twins, who were separated at seven years of age (see Chapter 6). Other environmental factors may be important. Toxic substances can induce conjoined twinning in hamsters but no other poisons have been found to cause human conjoining.

Philip Jones Griffiths, a photojournalist, has described his many visits to Vietnam in his book *Agent Orange: Collateral Damage in Vietnam* (2003). He visited the Tu Du Hospital in Ho Chi Minh City, where he was shown many deformed fetuses and babies preserved in jars of formaldehyde, including conjoined twins.

Vivian Rothstein also visited the Tu Du Hospital and her comments were published in the March/April 1993 issue of *Boston Review*, as follows:

> *There were a number of Siamese twins connected at different parts of their bodies, children with horribly misshapen heads and twisted bodies, others barely recognizable as human beings. They were being saved as a record of the genetic defects presumably resulting from the American use of Agent Orange and other defoliants in clearing the jungles and forests of Vietnam.*

Some members of our group took photos, but I was afraid to raise my camera to the accusing faces in the jars for fear I would see them peering back at me. Hospital patients and staff gathered outside in the hall to see our reactions – most of us were beyond words.

We walked into the "peace village" for handicapped children built with the support of European charities. Here we had a chance to see the living evidence of what hospital director Dr. Nguyen Thi Ngoc believes to be the genetic degradation which resulted when dioxin entered the food chain and the water supply of Vietnam.

Photographs of the preserved twins described above do not show any dates or other information on the jars. It is possible that some or all of these preserved twins were collected over many years prior to the war and thus were not attributable to the effects of poison.

A detailed review of the Agent Orange problem in Vietnam concluded that results from twenty-two studies support the hypothesis that exposure to Agent Orange is associated with a statistically significant increase in the risk of birth defects, especially of spina bifida. The review does not mention conjoined twins.

In 1983, during the first international conference on 'Long Term Consequences of Herbicides and Defoliants Used in Vietnam During the Wartime on Nature and Human Health' held in Ho Chi Minh City, scientists from twenty-two countries, including the USA, recognised that the incidences of five categories of birth defects were abnormally high in the south of Vietnam as compared with other countries in the world and in the region. They were neural tube defects, deformities of limbs, deformities of the sensory organs, conjoined twins and cleft palate and lip.

Dr James Clary, Air Force scientist, said that the US Air Force knew Agent Orange was far more hazardous to the health of humans than anyone would admit at the time: "When we initiated the herbicide programme in the 1960s we were aware of the potential for damage due to dioxin contamination in the herbicide. We were even aware that the military formulation had a higher dioxin concentration than the civilian version, due to the lower cost and speed of manufacture. However, because the material was to be used on the enemy, none of us were overly concerned."

The most comprehensive account of these matters that I have found is the book *Agent Orange: Apocalypse Viet Nam* (page 232) by André Bouny (in French). I believe we should accept his summing-up:

> *In the year 1980 Siamese twins in Viet Nam occurred so frequently that scientific opinion is that they are due to Agent Orange. Curent statistics indicate that this anomaly occurs about one in 50,000 to 100,000 births. More often in females. In 1986 the only maternity hospital of Tu Du had seen ten pairs of Siamese twins. That is to say 60 times the world average. (Translation by Ms Lisa Whitworth)*

In April 1975, President Ford formally renounced the first use of herbicides by the United States in future wars.

Diet and drugs

There is some inconclusive evidence, mainly from studies in experimental animals, that the ingestion of certain drugs may lead to conjoined twins. Examples include the tranquilliser prochlorperazine, which may have caused conjoined twins in rats, and griseofulvin, which may have been responsible in two human cases. Exposure to pesticides containing the element selenium, manganese deficiencies, exposure to butyric acid or acetone, infections and radiation have been postulated to induce conjoined twins in laboratory animals, and may be significant in humans.

So what is the orthodox scientific explanation for conjoined twinning? Apart from rarely identified environmental causes, *there isn't one!*

Mechanism of conjoined twinning

There is still debate about how conjoining occurs in the uterus. Is it as a result of fission or fusion?

Fission

This is the traditional theory. If the separation of monozygous twins occurs in the first three days after fertilisation the twins are completely separated by two layers of membrane, the amnion and chorion and they must remain as separate twins. If the separation occurs later then they may be separated by only the amnion and must also remain separate. Rarely, in about 1% of cases, no membrane separates them, so that the twins are touching each other. They are called monoamniotic.

The fission theory assumes that, if the division occurs later than eleven days after fertilisation, the division may be incomplete, resulting in conjoined twins within one amniotic cavity. The theory has a long tradition of orthodoxy.

Situs inversus (mirror imaging) in which internal organs appear on the opposite side to normal does not occur more frequently in twins than singletons but is more common in conjoined twins. This suggests fission.

Fusion

Aristotle favoured a fusion theory. Two embryos originally separate reach a partial fusion. This has been suggested again tentatively from time to time but, in recent years, has been argued strongly by Rowena Spencer, an American paediatric surgeon, in her book *Conjoined Twins*. She spent ten years studying as many reports of conjoined twinning as she could find. Her advocacy rests on this study of 1300 cases, which have been described in over 2000 scientific papers.

A little explanation of embryology is necessary in order to understand the fusion theory. The term embryo refers to the first two months of life. After that it is called the fetus (or foetus).

The embryo develops three layers called the ectoderm (outermost), mesoderm (middle) and entoderm (innermost). In the early stages, the ectoderm does not cover the entire embryo but, later on, it will form the skin and other structures. Ectoderm cannot fuse with ectoderm, so it is argued that fusion of two embryos always occurs where the ectoderm is deficient.

It is suggested that if monozygous twin embryos touch each other so that homologous (i.e. same or equivalent) parts which lack a covering of ectoderm come together, then fusion can be the result.

Investigators in the USA reported in 1997 that conjoined twins born in the Dominican Republic showed evidence of fusion of two embryos.

Although Spencer has described this in much greater detail than is possible here, it has by no means convinced all other scientists. The debate continues.

This chapter has included the appalling results of the use of radiation and chemicals in peace and war. Perhaps peacetime catastrophes cannot be entirely prevented but we can only hope that future warring nations will have learnt the lessons which humanity demands.

Chapter 11

What happens to conjoined twins?

What are the chances of survival?
Many conjoined twins abort spontaneously. Abortion is induced medically in others. Two surveys have been published. Of nearly 8 million births in the USA annually, about 40% of conjoined twins were stillborn. Of the liveborn twins, only about 25% survived long enough to be a candidate for surgery because many died soon after birth (known as neonatal deaths). The Red Cross Children's Hospital in Cape Town, with forty-two years of experience, reported that about 28% of conjoined twins are stillborn. This is in addition to abortions. About 54% of liveborn conjoined twins die immediately after birth. Of the liveborn, only about 18% survive to be candidates for possible surgery. Many have other congenital abnormalities. A few survive, sometimes even until adulthood, with or without separation surgery.

What happens before birth?
Antenatal diagnosis is very important so that appropriate care can be organised for the pregnancy and delivery, and for the

children. Before modern imaging techniques were developed the diagnosis was sometimes made by X-ray (a technique invented in 1895). One of the earliest X-rays ever taken, in 1897, was of conjoined twins taken after birth. Although the danger of conventional X-radiation in pregnancy must be very small, modern practice is to err on the side of safety, so X-rays are rarely taken during pregnancy. The methods described below are more effective and safer. As much detail as possible of the abnormality is determined so that the likely outcome for the twins can be predicted and treatment planned. The following techniques can now be performed.

Ultrasound scanning
Ultrasound scanning was first developed for use in pregnancy in 1958 by Ian Donald and others in Glasgow. Several years of development were required before it became universally available. The first ultrasound diagnosis of conjoined twins was made in 1976 at thirty-seven weeks of gestation. Where facilities are available, all pregnant women now have an ultrasound scan early in pregnancy. This may establish the diagnosis of conjoined twins or other anomalies or indicate the need for further investigations. Ultrasound is a high-frequency sound that cannot be heard. It travels through fluid and soft tissues but is reflected back as echoes when it hits a denser surface. As ultrasound hits different structures in the body of different densities it sends back echoes of varying strength, building up a two-dimensional picture. Three-dimensional colour ultrasound is also now possible. Real-time movement can be visualised and filmed. Prints and DVDs can be made, and copies given to the parents.

Whereas the scans are normally performed through the abdomen, conjoined twins were more recently diagnosed at ten weeks using trans-vaginal three-dimensional ultrasound. This means that the transmitter is inserted into the vagina, thus getting closer to the fetus and improving the image. There has been an example of a false diagnosis of conjoined twins that was made with ultrasound at nine weeks of gestation, the mistake being discovered a few weeks later. A false diagnosis is likely to be very distressing. The later an ultrasound scan is done, the more detail can be observed. However, early diagnosis is essential and is sought with the help of the following methods.

Echocardiography, or cardiac ultrasound
This uses standard ultrasound techniques to image two-dimensional slices of the fetal heart or hearts. The latest ultrasound systems now employ three-dimensional real-time imaging. This can be useful if conjoined twins are found to have a single heart or deformed hearts. The nature of any cardiac abnormality will help determine if separation surgery will be possible.

Computed tomography (CT)
CT makes use of computer-processed combinations of many very low dose X-ray measurements taken from different angles to produce cross-sectional (tomographic) images, virtual slices of specific areas of a scanned object, allowing the user to see inside the object. A three-dimensional image is made. The technique was developed in the 1960s and 1970s. It has been claimed that it is thanks to the success and generosity of The Beatles that EMI was able to fund research and build early models for medical use. For the investigation of conjoined twins, the minimal risks associated with the use of X-rays in this technique are considered justifiable.

Magnetic resonance imaging (MRI)

MRI is an imaging technique used in radiology to visualise detailed internal structures. It is considered to be safer than CAT scanning because no ionising radiation is used. The first report of its use in the study of conjoined twins came from Dallas, Texas in 1986. MRI machines use a powerful magnetic field to align the magnetisation of some atoms in the body, and radio-frequency fields to systematically alter the alignment of this magnetisation. This information is recorded to construct an image of the scanned area of the body. The resulting scans are very detailed and in colour. It is possible to use MRI to construct an actual computer model of the fetus before birth, which facilitates antenatal assessment.

Antenatal management

Prenatal diagnosis can be made from about ten weeks but more detail is seen as the pregnancy progresses. When as much information as possible has been obtained, the parents and medical team are able to consider what the prospects are for surgical separation. Some parents may request and be granted an induced abortion, if this is legally and morally acceptable. Legal abortion is especially likely to take place if investigation shows union of the hearts or brains, which would make successful separation with the survival of both twins impossible. In the UK, about three-quarters of conjoined-twin pregnancies are legally terminated. Thirty-six sets were legally aborted in the UK between 2006 and 2010. The decision may be difficult and unpleasant. Counselling and support are vital. Spontaneous abortion or the delivery of stillborn twins occurs when failure to survive is due to anomalies incompatible with life.

If it is decided to let the pregnancy continue, the family and medical staff will need to anticipate and prepare for considerable media interest, which could be a problem. Parents react to publicity in varying ways. Some prefer the absolute minimum of media involvement but that is likely to be difficult to achieve. Others may welcome publicity for its own sake or as a means of encouraging financial assistance. Whether publicity is welcome or not it will happen and may be distressing. For example, although the Fannings (see Chapter 6) encouraged publicity, they became distressed by misrepresentations and the use of distorted facts and by many telephone enquiries. So, in order to put the record straight, Larry Fanning, the father, wrote a book about it all called *Separated Angels* (1995). To avoid unacceptable publicity, parents may arrange an exclusive contract with a particular newspaper, for which they will be generously paid. Such an arrangement should not be regarded as greed; after all, coping with conjoined twins is likely to be difficult and very expensive. Medical staff will have to plan the best management, which includes arranging delivery in the most appropriate hospital where all necessary care can be given.

What happens during labour/delivery?

Throughout most of history, vaginal delivery was the only option. Unfortunately, the risks of any multiple pregnancy are greater than with a single pregnancy. However, with conjoined twins, the risks are even greater because a difficult, obstructed labour is likely to occur as one twin gets in the way of the other. When this happens, the twins and/or the mother may die unless expert care is available. Historically, such problems have usually not been recorded. However, nearly all the examples occurring before the twentieth century described in this book achieved a vaginal delivery. Vaginal delivery is more likely if the twins are small due to prematurity. Therefore, today, the safest option is nearly always a planned Caesarean section two or three weeks before the expected date of delivery. Paediatricians and special-care baby unit staff will be in attendance.

What happens after birth?

See the comment 'To let live or die?' in Chapter 12. Careful preparation is made to ensure survival if it is possible. The obstetrician hands over to the paediatricians, nurses and other ancillary staff. If there is the prospect of separation then there will be a detailed multidisciplinary assessment and further investigations. Before considering present-day surgery, let us look at the history of separation surgery.

History of separation surgery

Under early Roman law, abnormal children were put to death, successful separation of conjoined twins being impossible in virtually every case. This was probably the fate of conjoined twins in many parts of the world for many centuries, and remains so sometimes today. In Arabia, the twin brothers Hashim ibn Abd Manaf and 'Abd Shams were born with Hashim's leg attached to his twin brother's head, although one must doubt the authenticity of this. Hashim (441–497 CE) was accepted as the overall local leader, with the responsibility of providing for the pilgrims in the Ka'aba precincts, with the support of his brothers. Legend says that their father, Abd Manaf ibn Qusai, separated his conjoined sons with a sword and that some priests believed that the blood that had flowed between them signified future wars between their progeny. The prediction came true. Confrontations did occur between Banu al'Abbas and Banu Ummaya ibn 'Abd Shams.

Conjoined twins who lived in the tenth century CE in Byzantium (Constantinople) were reported in several contemporary documents. One of these is by Theophanes Continuatus, whose translated text includes the statement, "During these days [945 CE] a monster from Armenia appeared in the City. There were two boys... connected together from the Ombilic down to the lower abdomen, in position face to face." When one of the twins died, doctors separated them cleverly at the line of connection with the hope of saving the other, but after three days, he also died. Joannes Skylitzes, a Greek historian, reported another account of the same case in the eleventh century CE. Images from the thirteenth century show the operation. These are probably copies made more than a century after contemporary drawings.

No further attempts at separation were reported until the late seventeenth century, when the first known separation of live twins occurred. Elizabeth and Catherine were born on 23 November 1689 in Hüttingen, near Basle, Switzerland. The mother was forty-two-year-old Clementia Meijerin. Dr Emanuel Konig was claimed to be the surgeon but he was probably a witness. Dr Johannes Fatio was either the surgeon or a witness. Fatio died in 1691 but his description of the operation did not appear until 1762. The twins were joined by a band located between the xiphoid bone (the lowest part of the sternum) and the umbilicus, similar to that of the Bunkers (see Chapter 2). The umbilical cords were fused and contained two sets of three blood vessels. Several doctors were consulted. The surgeon tied silk ligatures around the band close to the abdomen of each twin and tightened them every day until, after nine days, on 3 December, the band could be safely divided. This means that the procedure was probably commenced on the day after birth. The twins survived but nothing further is known about them. Another early example was probably performed in India in the nineteenth century. The Bunkers could have been separated fairly easily if they had lived in the twentieth century, even though their livers were joined. Separation of the Boko twins in 1953 is described in Chapter 6. In 1996 it was estimated that there had been about 200 separation operations performed up until that point. There have been many more since. However, it has been observed that potential authors have an understandable reluctance to report their failures.

Contemporary surgery

Today, the right of conjoined twins to live and be treated is clearly morally and legally inviolate. Nevertheless, an example where the parents and doctor appear to have attempted to cause the death of conjoined twins by withholding nutrition is described in Chapter 12, together with other ethical issues.

The twentieth century saw big strides made in separation surgery due to greater technical knowledge, improved visualisation techniques and the increasing expectations of parents and medical personnel. The medical problems vary greatly depending on the nature of the abnormalities. Sometimes the joining tissue is limited so that separation is easy. In many cases, however, separation can be very complicated and difficult, resulting in lengthy operations involving a large multidisciplinary team. The duration of separation surgery often lasts well over twelve hours. The longest operation I have seen reported was the separation of the Shrestha twins born in Nepal in 2000, which is reputed to have lasted ninety hours. Well over 50% of conjoined twins have other congenital anomalies in addition to the conjoined state, which may influence treatment. Such additional anomalies are likely to be operated on at a later date. Three-dimensional modelling and surgical rehearsal may help pre-operative assessment.

Separation is likely to be possible if there are two separate brains and two separate hearts. Even if the brains or hearts are joined it is sometimes possible to separate and reconstruct them, or to reconstruct one of the hearts. Continuing deformity after surgery is likely, especially when limbs are absent. In some cases, separation may be necessary without delay in order to prevent the twins dying or to save the life of one of them. If possible, it is preferable for separation to be delayed for a few months so that the often complicated surgery can be planned and the infants can gain pre-operative strength. Separation during the first year of life helps to avoid psychological trauma to the twins, which can occur if there is late separation. Sometimes, when it is clear that there will be insufficient skin to cover a defect after separation, a balloon is inserted beneath the skin several weeks before the operation. This is gradually inflated with silicone or foam to stretch the skin, so that an excess of skin becomes available for grafting.

Even when major surgery is technically possible, in many parts of the world there may be insuperable barriers of cost and the availability of medical facilities. This is discussed in the Ethics section (see Chapter 12). The event is likely to be widely reported in the media. Dealing with the media may be tricky. A small number of surgical teams and hospitals have acquired experience of this difficult kind of surgery, for example Great Ormond Street Hospital in London, the Red Cross Children's Hospital in Cape Town, the Children's Hospital of Philadelphia, the Hospital for Sick Children, Toronto, Johns Hopkins University Medical Center, Baltimore, Maryland, the Children's Hospital, Boston, Massachusetts, the Texas Children's Hospital, Houston, Texas and Xinhua Hospital in China (apologies to any I have missed). The technical challenge is so great that in order for the best results to be obtained it is advisable that expertise be confined to relatively few hospitals and surgeons.

The challenges involved in surgery can best be illustrated by considering the Binder twins (see Chapter 6). Patrick and Benjamin Binder were born by Caesarean section on 2 February 1987 at Ulm, Germany. The backs of their heads were joined and they shared some skull bone and some intracranial blood vessels. Their brains were fused and shared the sagittal sinus, the major vein draining blood from the brain. Together, the twins weighed 8 lbs 14 oz. The German doctors sought the help of Ben Carson, an American surgeon at Johns Hopkins University Medical Center. (Incidentally, Carson, now retired, unsuccessfully sought to be the Republican Party Presidential Candidate in 2016.) Dr Carson has described what happened in some detail in his book *Gifted Hands* (1990). Together with other colleagues, he went to Germany to assess whether separation would be possible.* They agreed to make the attempt. The twins were four months old. One of the problems with separation was that there would not be enough skin to cover the resulting raw area. So, while in Germany, they inserted inflatable silicone balloons under the scalps. These would be gradually inflated to slowly stretch the skin so that sufficient skin would be available following separation. The main problem, however, was to separate the brains while causing the minimum of damage. This was a huge challenge. The twins were transferred to Johns Hopkins University Medical Center. Extensive and detailed preparations were required, taking five months. These included adaptation of the operating theatre and the assembling of a multidisciplinary team of experts including anaesthetists, paediatricians, nurses and others. Then there were five three-hour dress rehearsals using life-sized dolls attached at the head with Velcro.

Finally, the operation began at 7.15 am on 5 September 1987; the twins were seven months old. The parents were kept informed of progress during the operation. Intravenous and intra-arterial catheters enabled accurate monitoring of the twins' condition. The skin was incised. Portions of the skulls were removed and kept for subsequent reconstruction. The membranes covering the brains were divided and the arteries and veins were also divided. All this required delicate dissection. Considerable bleeding occurred, which was controlled by transfusion and by sewing muscle patches into the bleeding area. To facilitate separation of the vascular structures it was necessary to cool the blood from ninety-five to sixty-eight degrees Fahrenheit [35 to 20 degrees C]. by using a heart-lung bypass for each twin. The hearts could then be stopped for up to an hour, during which the twins were separated. Each then required rapid repair of blood vessels before normal blood flow was restored; Carson worked on one twin and Dr Dolin Long on the other. New sagittal veins were constructed using portions of the pericardium (the membrane that covers the heart), which had previously been removed for this purpose. They completed this in just under the hour. On restoring the hearts, there was considerable bleeding from the many small vessels. This was aggravated by the anticoagulants which had been necessary. The surgeons took three hours to control the bleeding while blood transfusion continued. The available supply of blood was only just enough as sixty units had been required. One unit is 470 ml, so that about forty-eight pints were used. The operation had lasted twenty-two hours. At later dates, on twenty-two occasions, plastic surgeons restored the skulls using titanium meshes covering a paste of crushed bone from the shared portion of the twins' skulls.

Unfortunately, two years after the separation, the twins were both brain-damaged, which is likely to be permanent. Patrick Binder remains in a vegetative state, said David Nichols, a paediatric anaesthetist at Johns Hopkins Children's

Center who participated in the surgery. Referring to the other twin, Benjamin, Nichols said that he is improving, but is "clearly not normal and developmentally delayed". Carson said, "In a technological star wars sort of way, the operation was a fantastic success, but as far as having normal children, I don't think it was all that successful." The medical bills totalled $300,000, and were paid for by West Germany's health insurance.

There are only about 200 separated conjoined twins currently living around the globe. If separation is impossible or is decided against, conjoined twins may live to adulthood, which is not necessarily an unmitigated disaster. For example, the Bunker and Schappell twins seem to have had at least fairly contented lives. This topic is considered further in Chapter 13. Most hospitals are likely to follow the principles set down by Great Ormond Street Hospital in London, which are shown in Chapter 12. With regard to the death of unseparated conjoined twins, invariably when one dies the other dies immediately or within a few hours. Clearly it would be a most unhealthy and untenable situation if one twin were to continue to live while attached to its dead twin. It seems that nature provides the solution, but that this is not always the case in fiction (see Chapter 15).

What about future pregnancies?

The parents of conjoined twins will want to know what the risk of having another set is. They can be reassured. There may be a greater chance of a multiple pregnancy but no greater risk of another set of conjoined twins. I have found only one example of a second set having the same parents.

177

Chapter 12

Ethics

To abort or not? *That is a question*

In many countries, medically induced abortion of a non-viable fetus is legal under certain circumstances. A significant congenital abnormality is usually an adequate legal reason. In some countries, abortion on demand is also legal with or without a medical reason. Legal abortion is to be distinguished from spontaneous abortion, often called miscarriage, in which the pregnancy is expelled spontaneously as a result of some medical condition. Conjoined twins are prone to spontaneous abortion and also to stillbirth.

Whether abortion is ever morally acceptable continues to be debated (pro-life versus pro-choice). Many people have religious scruples against abortion which may be altered when they are confronted with conjoined fetuses in the uterus. However, if conjoined twins are diagnosed early enough, legal abortion (where allowed) is a safe option that many parents will wish to consider. Illegal abortion, sometimes called 'back-street abortion', is dangerous but may be resorted to when legal abortion is unavailable. Abortion of conjoined fetuses that occurs, either legally, illegally or spontaneously, thus significantly reduces the number who are born alive or stillborn.

To let live or die? *That is another question*

In some societies, deformed infants were and still are killed or allowed to die. This may take place because of superstitious beliefs or simply as the most expedient solution to the horror felt by the parents and others.

A modern incident where leaving conjoined twins to die was attempted was reported in several issues of the *Washington Post* in 1981. Conjoined twins were born in Illinois. The parents and obstetrician agreed to leave them without food or water. Later, a complaint was made to the Department of Children and Family Services, which resulted in the twins being placed in state custody, where they survived. The parents and physician were indicted on charges of attempted murder and child neglect. A month later the charges were dropped, the judge ruling that there was insufficient evidence. The twins were returned to the parents under supervision and, a year later, they were successfully separated surgically.

Infanticide is a universal crime and most would regard it as morally unjustified, however deformed the infant or infants may be. Some may argue that what amounts to euthanasia could be justified in such circumstances, although it would of course be without the consent of the patients.

One soul or two? *A question unlikely today*

In 1533 conjoined twin girls died in Santo Domingo in the Dominican Republic. A priest had baptised each of them but he was concerned that perhaps they only had one soul, in which case he would have committed an error. So he ordered a post-mortem examination in the hope of discovering the truth! Each child had a complete set of organs, so the priest felt vindicated in assuming they had two souls.

To separate or not to separate? *That is a big question*

Marlene Cady, the mother of conjoined girls Ruthie and Verena (see Chapter 6), has stated, "We have to remember that it's not just a matter of separating them physically, but also psychologically, spiritually, and emotionally." Wise words.

If separation is considered after infancy (i.e. above the age of one year), there is the possibility that the twins may have developed emotional and psychological bonds, the severing of which could be traumatic. Professor Lewis Spitz of Great Ormond Street Hospital described an example of three-year-old twins called Katie and Eilish who were separated but Katie died. He commented, "Eilish was clearly devastated that her twin had disappeared and for one year after surgery she would not talk to me."

Professor Heinze Rode of Cape Town has claimed, in relation to a particular case, "You cannot go through Africa in this [conjoined] situation, you will be an outcast, you will become a monster, you will be a curiosity, you will become a showpiece." He also argues that another reason for separation is that even genetically identical conjoined twins will grow up with different personalities, thus increasing the imperative for separation in that continent. He seems to imply that separation could be appropriate at any age. Is this reasonable?

However, when considering surgical separation, there are four possible scenarios depending on the nature of the join and the opinions of parents, doctors and maybe the law and others.

Firstly, there are examples where separation is technically straightforward, resulting in two normal or virtually normal individuals. There is usually no ethical problem involved. For example, the Bunker twins (see Chapter 2) could be safely separated today, although in their day there would have been a significant risk because their livers were joined and their peritoneal cavities would have had to be opened, with the risk of infection. Nevertheless, separation would have deprived them of their ability to make their fortune through showbiz. This issue has also been illustrated by Alice Dreger, who has pointed out that the McKoy twins (see Chapter 3) became wealthy through being exhibited but, had they been born separate, they would probably have led a miserable life as exploited slaves. Nevertheless, it would surely have been going too far, and indeed would have been unethical, to have denied separation on the grounds that, while joined, they would have been able to earn a living.

Secondly, there are examples where separation is possible but would be difficult and expensive. Surgery may involve the risk of one or both twins dying or being left with serious disability, but the survival of both is possible without surgery. There have been several such cases in recent years because surgical technology has advanced and so has the ambition and experience of surgeons, together with the expectations of parents. The parents and surgeons will need to weigh up the pros and cons. They will need to consider the risks and to compare the outcome with and without surgery. The situation may be fraught with distress, anxiety and uncertainty. This has been discussed in Chapter 11.

Decisions about separation are nearly always made by the parents and doctors when the twins are in infancy, but sometimes the twins reach maturity and can then make their own decision, an example being the Bijani twins (see Chapter 7), who are apparently the only adult conjoined twins to have opted for separation. Bearing this in mind, perhaps we should agree with Dreger, who discusses the issue in detail and claims that, "The available documentation concludes that the desire to remain together is so widespread among communicating conjoined twins as to be practically universal... therefore given the current state of our knowledge, I do not think we can rationally conclude that being separated is always better than being conjoined." She comments that when surgery is likely to result in one or two disabled individuals, is this something we would do to a singleton? She concludes, "Conjoined twins tend to grow into a body that they're born with, the same way the rest of us do and so they're born into this body joined and they will develop an understanding of their lives as joined. These are very difficult cases and I'm not saying there's a simple answer, though we have at least to take into account what conjoined twins themselves would say." Parents and surgeons usually believe in separation if possible. Regarding this view, Dreger comments, "In short, parents and surgeons are far from emotionally objective in the decisions they make on behalf of the children."

However, even when surgery is appropriate, there may be practical obstacles. The family may be unable to afford expensive surgery or there may be no suitable surgical facilities available, a situation that can occur in developing countries. Sometimes such twins may be able to undergo surgery if they can obtain generous support from friends or charities or their government. For example, the parents of the Lakebergs (see Chapter 6) in the USA were uninsured. The issue of whether huge expense in return for a doubtful result could be justified was widely discussed. In fact, the cost of over $1 million was shared by Medicaid and the hospital.

Perhaps we should accept the opinion of Ronald Dworkin, Professor of Jurisprudence at Oxford University and Professor of Law at New York University, who wrote, "Any nation that tried to provide every possible treatment, no matter how expensive, even when the treatment had only a small chance of working, would have little money left for obviously valuable medical policies." The Lakebergs also faced the problem that the twins only had one heart and so they also come under the third scenario discussed below.

To what extent should a country pay for the treatment of foreigners? Twins Sarah and Sarahi Morales, born in Tijuana, Mexico in 1996, were separated in San Diego, California. The cost was met from various sources but the hospital was criticised by many for providing so much care to Mexican citizens. Similarly, San Diego Hospital was criticised for paying for the separation of Hever and Romain Moreno, who belonged to a Mexican family, even though the twins were born in the USA and so were US citizens.

Thirdly, there are examples where separation is only possible with the death of one twin, as would be the case if there were only one heart. This group poses the most difficult ethical dilemma. Such operations have been called 'sacrifice surgeries'. The issues involved are best examined by looking at five actual examples.

Example 1

George Annas, Professor of Health Law at Boston, has described a case that illustrates the kind of arguments that have been put forward. In 1977, at the Children's Hospital in Philadelphia, twins could only be separated if one of them died. The Jewish parents wanted sanction from their rabbi, the Catholic nurses wanted sanction from their priest and the surgeon wanted sanction from the court. The rabbi argued that the case was analogous to that of two men jumping from a burning plane. The parachute of one man does not open but he clings to the legs of the other, whose parachute cannot support both of them. The man with the parachute would be justified in kicking off the other to save his own life because the life of the other man was 'designated for death'. The Catholics argued that an action that has both a good and a bad effect is justified if the good act does not come about because of the bad act. The operation would be justified because its intention would be to save a life, not to destroy one. The doctors, afraid of homicide charges, argued that, as the twins had only one heart, they were essentially one person. They also debated another scenario similar to the parachute argument. This case went to court. The three-judge panel heard all these arguments. After only a few minutes they authorised the operation, which was performed the next day. As expected, the twin with no heart died. The surviving twin died after three months, although this is irrelevant to the ethical arguments.

Example 2

Conjoined twins Ruthie and Verena Cady (see Chapter 6), who were born in 1984, could only have been separated if one was sacrificed. The parents decided against separation. The mother said, "I don't know that the rest of us really have the capability to make that decision for them. Ruthie and Verena taught us so much. They were a perfect example of sisterhood and unity." Two years later they both died.

Example 3

In later years there seems to have been less anxiety about such issues in the USA. Annas describes conjoined twins born in 1987 who were separated with the death of one of them at the Children's Hospital, Philadelphia. The surgeon did not seek immunity from prosecution but the hospital lawyers obtained an assurance from the District Attorney, who promised immunity but thought this provision unnecessary. Annas concludes, "It is better to try to save one life than to passively observe two lives end. Both law and ethics support reasonable medical attempts to separate Siamese twins with conjoined hearts."

Example 4

Angela and Amy Lakeberg (see Chapter 6) were born on 29 June 1993 at Loyola University Medical Center in Chicago. Although they were Roman Catholics, the parents considered having an abortion but decided against. The Loyola Ethics Committee advised against separation, explicitly not because of the parents' Roman Catholic affiliation but because of the very small chance of one twin surviving while the other died. It is thought that another reason for the Ethics Committee rejecting surgery was the fact that the family was dysfunctional, with a suboptimal home environment. Dr Muraskas said, "Let's feed them and keep them warm. Let's put them in God's hands so to speak." Passing the buck to God: is that right?

The Loyola physicians advised discontinuing life support and letting the twins die naturally. The parents rejected this and found surgeons at the Children's Hospital of Philadelphia who were willing to operate. The surgeons argued that it was the parents' right to make a decision, even though they estimated the chance of one twin surviving as only 1%.

Eventually, separation was performed in Philadelphia on 30 August 1993, when the twins were six weeks old. The surgeons had to decide which one would die. They chose Amy. Angela did survive but died at ten months of pneumonia aggravated by her deformities. Her death is irrelevant to the ethical argument.

Dworkin stated, "True respect for human life was sacrificed at Philadelphia, to bad slogans about sanctity of life and rescue, and, perhaps, to a dangerous love for heroic medicine for its own sake." This opinion was both supported and opposed by many. Dr John LaPuma, an ethicist at Chicago's Lutheran General Hospital, said, "Parents like the Lakebergs should be told that the surgery would be a research experiment, not a treatment… it shouldn't be portrayed as being for the babies' good." Would that last opinion be the most honest?

In the USA and elsewhere there has been considerable debate. Stephen Lammers provided a comment from the USA: "It is grimly ironic that we live in a society that permits a procedure such as the one performed in the Lakeberg case, but at the same time permits… its infant-mortality rate to be one of the highest in the industrialized world. Such a state of affairs cannot be defended on any grounds."

It was argued that no one has the right to decide that another should die, as happened in this case. However, a decision not to operate would have killed both in time. With the benefit of hindsight, not to operate would probably have been the right decision, as was made originally at Loyola. But no one had hindsight or foresight.

Example 5

In the case of Rosie and Gracie Attard (see Chapter 7), born on Gozo, an island near Malta, in 2000 and then transferred to Manchester, England, the Roman Catholic parents refused an operation because they accepted the orthodox Catholic view that deliberately causing the death of one twin, even in order to save the other, cannot be justified. On the other hand, it seems that the feelings of the parents were also influenced by the prospect of returning to Malta with one handicapped child, with all the problems and expense that would have involved. Nevertheless, they stuck to their refusal. In effect they were accepting the death of both children rather than the prospect of caring for one handicapped child.

One doctor argued that, "It is more logical to think of it [Rosie] as a tumour, a growth that is sapping life. By giving it a name, these poor parents have created a situation where they think they are killing a baby by having the operation. But what they are calling Rosie is really a tumour." If one should have a troubled conscience about the operation, perhaps that is the way to look at it.

The surgeons and the Health Authority in Manchester took the case to court to find out if surgery without parental consent would be lawful. The court found that it would be lawful. Then the Vatican offered to arrange for the twins to be transferred to an Italian hospital without undergoing surgery. However, the parents instead appealed against the court's decision. The appeal was heard by a three-judge panel, all of whom agreed with the original judge's conclusion that surgery was allowable. It has been well established, at least in Britain, that a court can overrule a parent's refusal of treatment for their child if that refusal is not in the best interests of the child. An example of this is the overruling of parents who are Jehovah's Witnesses and are opposed to the treatment of their child who has haemolytic disease of the newborn which, if untreated with a blood transfusion, would result in death or severe disability. Ian McEwan's novel/film *The Children Act* discusses these issues and also describes the severe stress that the judges may have to endure. A fuller account of the appeal hearing can be read in Alice Dreger's book *One of Us*, together with an account of the considerable debate that surrounded it, and also a detailed analysis of the ethics involved. She reports that, up until 2004, there had been at least eleven 'sacrifice surgeries.'

The parents capitulated (presumably this means that they agreed to surgery). The operation took place on 6–7 November 2000 and took twenty hours. As expected, Rosie died and Gracie survived. The doctors received a lot of threats and hate mail. When Gracie was ten months old she returned with her parents to Gozo. The parents were quoted as saying, "In the end we are happy that the decision to separate was taken by the judges... of course we're now happy that we still have Gracie." A description of the Attard case from the points of view of a lawyer, a theologian and the surgeon can be found in the transcripts of speeches given in 2002. This includes the statement by Lord Justice Ward that, "the law must allow an escape by choosing the lesser of two evils".

As reported in Chapter 7, Gracie was alive and well at the age of fifteen, but this happy outcome is irrelevant to the ethical issues.

With regard to the situation in Britain, the legalities were well summed up by Alexander McCall Smith when he was Professor of Medical Law at the University of Edinburgh. Referring to the Attard twins, and to British law, he wrote, "The judges might decide to favour one child over the other, but they could not authorise a procedure that could amount to homicide. At this point the principle of necessity entered the courtroom. Necessity is a loose criminal law defence that may authorise an otherwise criminal act provided that the act is the lesser of two evils. This judgement holds that exceptional necessity may justify the taking of a life when an inescapable choice has to be made between two persons."

When decision making is difficult the parents may ask, "What is the percentage chance of success?" The surgeons may believe that surgery should not be attempted as the chance of success is so small, so they make the reply, "one or two percent." The parents may say, "That's good enough, let's go ahead." But in such a situation, should the surgeons undertake a long, difficult and expensive operation that they know is virtually futile?

It is not only the parents who may have to shoulder the burden of difficult decisions. What about the surgeons who are to destroy a life even though they have decided that in their opinion it is the right thing to do? In the case of the

Lakebergs, one of the surgeons said that, when they came to cut off the blood supply to Amy, "nothing was said, but I know everybody felt it". In the case of the Attards, two paediatric surgeons, Alan Dickson and Adrian Bianchi, elected to make the final cut together as they felt it was inappropriate for one person to shoulder the burden of consigning Rosie to death. Dickson recalls, "It was a very intense moment. We looked at each other because we all knew what we were doing at the time. The theatre was very quiet. People knew what was happening and it was done with great respect… it was a shared experience which I have to say I didn't relish."

It may seem that, in all cases, separation should be attempted if at all feasible. However, the moral issues may not be so simple, as has been well expounded by Dreger. She refers to the traditional view expressed in the Judaic tradition that somehow a deformed body is inferior. For example, in the Old Testament of the Bible, Moses tells Aaron, "None of your descendants who has any physical defect may present the food offering to me. This applies for all time to come. No man who has any physical defect may make the offering; no one who is blind, lame, disfigured, or deformed; no one with a crippled hand or foot; no one who is a hunchback or a dwarf; no one with any eye or skin disease; and no eunuch" (Leviticus 21.17b–20). Eventually this attitude has been superseded so that civilised society now accepts the words of St. Paul that, "You are all one [i.e. equal]" (Galatians 3.28b). Thus the defective, even conjoined, twins have a claim to equality. When conjoined twins have a chance to make a choice, as in adulthood, they almost invariably decide to stay joined. Some examples have been described. The Bijani twins are the exception as they decided on separation. Dreger's implication is that maybe some twins separated in childhood would have decided against separation if they had grown up to have a choice. She points out that parents and surgeons are far from emotionally objective in the decisions they make on behalf of the children.

Fourthly, there are examples where separation is impossible, with the outcomes being either the early death of both twins or survival with permanent joining. In the past, survival often meant that public exhibition was the only way to survive. This is discussed below and in Chapter 13.

In 2000, the BBC showed a discussion involving two sets of conjoined twins who reached adulthood without separation (Masha and Dasha Krivoshlyapova and the Schappells), together with doctors and others who were involved. The ethical issues were discussed, and both sets of twins argued that they would never want separation. Lori Schappell said, "We fully believe that God made us this way and He had a purpose for us and you do not ruin what God has made. We still live normal productive everyday lives." The doctors, including Jonathan Peter of Cape Town, where up until then there had been the world's most extensive experience of separation surgery, and Professor Spitz of London, also a very experienced practitioner, argued for separation whenever possible. The discussion and transcript of the broadcast* is well worth seeing by anyone who would like to get close to these problems and who wishes to understand and empathise with those most closely involved.

Strange as it may seem, some conjoined twins have led fairly normal lives. Where there's a will there's a way. Some problems can be overcome. The human body and spirit can be amazingly adaptable, as many disabled people can testify.

Another aspect is the effect of public opinion, which can be expressed with great emotion and therefore may lack objectivity. Publicity may influence the parents and others. One doctor in the USA, referring to a case in which a difficult decision had to be made, stated, "The major problem when this critical decision was about to be made was the media. The family was essentially addicted to it, and the 'go for glory and defy all odds' mentality prevailed." Another doctor stated, "Conjoined twins should not be subject to the circus like atmosphere generated by the news media to satisfy the public's morbid interest in human suffering." Some hospitals have attempted to keep proceedings secret so as to avoid this problem. However, when the secret is out, a newspaper may offer the parents generous terms in return for exclusive reporting. Who can blame the parents for accepting, especially as the lifelong care of one or two disabled children is likely to be expensive? An expert in Chicago commented, "In the United States competition among hospitals has given rise to public relations departments, which relentlessly present newsworthy events to the public. This type of publicity is pernicious and may be detrimental to care."

Many, and perhaps most, hospitals follow the guidelines of Great Ormond Street Hospital in London, which are as follows:

> *Where separation is feasible with a reasonable chance of success it should be carried out; when surgery is not possible, custodial care should be offered and nature allowed to take its course; where one twin is dead or has a lethal abnormality and cannot survive independently from its normal twin and, if not operated on both twins could die, separation to save the healthy twin should be attempted.*

Controversies remain, however.

   * BBC Science and Nature – Horizon – Conjoined Twins

What about sex? *Yet another question*

For some people this constitutes an impossible dilemma and they believe that sex without privacy would be immoral or at least undesirable. However, for conjoined twins, flirtation may be relatively easy but progressing to falling in love and/or marriage presents obvious problems as well as possibilities. Some may be shocked but love can conquer all! And has done so. Houdini taught Daisy and Violet Hilton how one of them could withdraw mentally while the other enjoyed sex. One switched off while the other switched on! Other conjoined twins have testified to a similar ability. Both the Bunkers married and both had many children. The stories described in earlier chapters illustrate various other scenarios. For some conjoined twins their enforced companionship provides a substitute for the companionship of marriage. Dreger points out that, when conjoined twins have sex, it is like having sex one on one; the other one simply zones out and pays attention to something else. Compassionate society should surely accept whatever decisions these twins make.

There have been conjoined twins with only one set of male genitalia (see Chapter 6). Separation has been achieved by giving one twin the male genitalia and reconstructing the other as female, thus constituting a sex change from male to female. There have been at least three examples. One can only imagine the difficult and stressful feelings of all those concerned.

Millie and Christine McKoy even allowed a detailed description of their sexual anatomy to be printed in their pamphlets. The fact that this description had been compiled by doctors enabled them to hope that any charge of sensational titillation or pornography would be avoided. It must have been a matter of opinion whether that hope was fulfilled. However, any salacious information is likely to have brought in the showbiz pundits.

Dreger sums up as follows:

Whether or not both are 'having sex' with the third person in the equation depends on how you think about 'having sex'... From my studies, I would postulate that conjoined twins probably end up having less sex than average people, and that is not only because sex partners are harder to find when you're conjoined. Conjoined twins simply may not need sex-romance partners as much as the rest of us do. Throughout time and space, they have described their condition as something like being attached to a soul mate. They may just not desperately need a third, just as most of us with a second to whom we are very attached don't need a third.

To live in normal society or to be secluded? *A final question*
Conjoined twins who are not separated pose many questions for themselves and society: How to live? How should responsibility for care be shared between relatives, friends and society? How can superstitious attitudes, which can result in cruelty, be countered? How much medical investigation beyond the requirements of care and treatment is justified?

Many years ago, shame and embarrassment on the part of conjoined twins and the public encouraged seclusion. Public opinion may have even insisted on seclusion. The need to exhibit for money broke down this barrier but such twins must at least have felt uncomfortable, as their exposure to the public was only possible via paying customers. Some conjoined twins have welcomed exhibition, even though they may not have enjoyed it, because they depended on the income. In more recent times, there has developed much greater tolerance of all kinds of abnormality. Civilised society now makes big efforts to help such persons live as normal a life as possible.

The increasing popularity of sport for the disabled is an example. The Paralympics take place, one assumes, without any uncharitable thoughts.

With regard to public exhibition for money, opinions have been controversial but have evolved. How would any of us feel if we were suddenly and unexpectedly confronted by conjoined twins in a public place? Compassion and good manners demand that we should resist the desire to stand and stare. Yet if there is payment to be made that the twins depend on for their livelihoods then we may wish to contribute. When the Bunkers were exhibited, a London newspaper commented, "People would be apt to imagine that there would be something unpleasant in the exhibition of two human beings joined together, but such is not the case. On the contrary, they must excite the most pleasurable sensation in all those who are capable in taking delight in beholding a perfect picture of innocence and happiness – for such is the appearance the two lads present." Today, this seems patronising but, in those days, prosperity for such individuals depended upon exhibition.

People should beware of feeling or showing pity. Pity implies that the subject is suffering, when they may well not be. When Dreger asked Lori Schappell how she felt about pity she bristled, saying that as soon as she saw such a 'pity conversation' starting, she would end it or leave it. Patty Hensel, the mother of conjoined girls, said, "People say, 'We pray for you and the girls'... But we don't need anyone to feel sorry for us." This degree of understanding and acceptance makes it much easier for conjoined twins to live as normal a life as possible. They then have the right to make decisions, including whether to be separated or not, if they live to have that option.

Chapter 13

Psychology

Should conjoined twins be regarded as one or two persons? Until the twentieth century it was common to regard them as one. For example, the McKoy twins, born in 1851, were called Millie-Christine and their shows were advertised as "The Double-Headed Girl". The clergy agonised: Did conjoined twins have one or two souls? Was the soul in the head or the heart? Should there be one or two baptisms? The Bunkers amusingly presented themselves as one person when buying a single train ticket, which caused trouble. Nowadays, there is no dispute: two heads means two persons, and one head means one person, and that is the approach of psychological studies.

What determines personality? Nature and nurture, meaning heredity and environment. Is there anything else? Twin studies should help. The first significant study was by Francis Galton in 1883. He compared a group of identical twins (MZ) with a group of fraternal twins (DZ), studying mainly life events. (Identical twins are never exactly identical.)

Many investigations have followed, in particular the extensive studies of Horatio H. Newman and others, published in 1937 (*Twins: a Study of Heredity and Environment*). A useful approach has been to compare MZ twins who have been brought up together with those who have been brought up separately. Such studies enable a comparison between nature and nurture, because the former have the same nature and nurture whereas the latter have different nurtures.

In fact, the personalities and behaviour of MZ twins, even those brought up together, can be strikingly different. Newman et al. summarise some of their findings as follows: "One of the most striking facts that came to light in our studies of identical twins reared together is that the two members of a pair are never truly identical but differ more or less with respect to all their characters and that they differ sometimes to a disconcerting degree." They suggest that this finding may have something to do with the prenatal inequality of the blood supply to each twin. This is explained in more detail below. They also discuss the possible significance of physical asymmetry, but their discussion is frankly confusing and therefore does not help much. Nevertheless, several other investigators agree that identical twins, including conjoined ones, do tend to have greater differences than fraternal twins, which is not what one would expect.

Newman et al. were forced to conclude that, "If at the inception of this research project over ten years ago, the authors entertained any hope of reaching a definitive solution of the general nature-nurture problem... they were disappointed."

Sir Cyril Burt's studies from 1955 of identical twins reared apart claimed to prove that genetics alone determined intelligence. Sadly, it was later shown that his work and conclusions were fraudulent.

James Shields, in his book *Monozygotic Twins, Brought Up Apart and Brought Up Together* (1962), compared forty-four pairs of identical twins brought up apart with forty-four pairs brought up together. He concluded that environment could contribute to differences in intelligence. The twins resembled each other in extraversion and neuroticism. Personality differences were also similar in both groups, which strongly suggested the importance of heredity. Nevertheless, Shields found that twins brought up together could differ quite widely. He also commented that, "much human behaviour appears to be the result of individual unpredictability". J. David Smith (*Psychological Profiles of Conjoined Twins: Heredity, Environment, and Identity*; 1988) reviewed the studies mentioned above and found weaknesses. For example, so-called separated identical twins were often not completely separated. This suggests that finding similar IQs could have been due not only to genetics but also to similar environments. His observations were later confirmed in 1984 by Richard Lewontin, Stephen Rose and Leon Kamin.

Nancy Segal (herself a fraternal twin), in her book *Entwined Lives: Twins and What They Tell Us About Human Behaviour* (2000), published a comprehensive and perceptive survey. She emphasised that, although conjoined twins have substantially the same environment, there can be substantial differences between them.

The differences between conjoined twins that do occur are likely to be due at least partially to free will, although the mechanistically minded may doubt the existence of this. Samuel Johnson is reputed to have said, "All science is against freedom of the will; all common sense for it." But even scientists have common sense and so should allow free will a place.

There remain interesting questions regarding conjoined twins: Do these studies throw any light on the psychology of conjoined twins who share nature and nurture for their whole lives, and so may one expect them to have virtually identical personalities? To what extent are their personalities similar or different, and how do they compare with non-conjoined twins?

When Smith studied the psychology of conjoined twins, he found that, "in every instance I found the same situation, Siamese twins were always very different in traits, temperament, and personality". He therefore found that heredity and environment are not the only determinants of personality. He claimed that heredity "creates a physiology which allows us to be creative and flexible individuals". With regard to environment he stated, "The environment not only moulds us but also offers us a continually changing spectrum of opportunities." Thus individuals are more than the product of nature and nurture. The influence of free will produces a third factor which Smith calls 'intentionality'.

Therefore, psychological studies seem to lead to the conclusion that personality is determined by heredity plus environment (not heredity versus environment) plus intentionality.

What can we learn from the personalities of conjoined twins who have lived long enough to answer the question, what determines personality? For example, the Bunkers, Hensels, Schappells and Hiltons?

What can we learn from the Bunker twins? There were several significant differences between them. Edward Bulwer-Lytton's long poem *The Siamese Twins: A Satirical Tale of the Times*, published in 1831 when the twins were aged twenty, explores their differences (see Chapter 2). While the Bunker twins were sailing for the USA, Captain Coffin observed differences between them. Chang was mentally brighter and could be irritable while Eng was quieter and had wider intellectual interests. Professor Tucker gave psychological tests to the Bunker twins. In a paper called *Psychological Observations of the Siamese Twins* written in 1836, and published in 1841, he recorded his findings. There were considerable differences between the twins. Dr John Warren also examined them, finding that, "They differ in intellectual vigour, one being irritable and the other mild." Chang was fond of alcohol while Eng was not. A hotel bill from 1870 includes the purchase of two bottles of wine, eight bottles of beer, one bottle of cognac and one bottle of whisky on just one day. Presumably this was for Chang, although we do not know how long that supply lasted or whether it was shared with others. Judge Graves, who knew the Bunkers well, recorded his observations after their death, describing them as having very good memories and friendly personalities. They were fond of literature, including Shakespeare, Byron and Pope. Nevertheless, he observed their differences: "They were men of as distinct mental individuality as any two brothers. On one occasion they actually fought each other."

What can we learn from the Hilton twins? Dr Helen Koch studied the Hiltons at the age of fourteen and compared the results with those for non-conjoined identical and fraternal twins. Daisy Hilton's intellectual and scholastic abilities were superior to those of Violet, although their temperaments were similar. In 1932, Ernest Seeman and Robert Saudek found that Daisy liked the romantic literature of Conrad, Sabatini and J. M. Barrie, whereas Violet was more serious and "liked to pit her young mind against the unsolved mysteries of time".

What can we learn from the Schappell twins? Here we find a radical difference between them as Lori/Reba, who is of course genetically female, decided to come out as psychologically male at the age of forty-six and changed her name to George. He also had a successful career as a country singer. In spite of these differences, these twins seem to get on very well together.

What can we learn from the Hensel twins? While physical activity demands close cooperation, their personalities show many differences. They can study separately, Abby preferring maths while Brittany prefers writing. One prefers pink and the other blue. One enjoys animals while the other likes art. They prefer different kinds of food.

These examples confirm what the psychologists found, namely that conjoined twins are likely to have considerable differences, even if this seems paradoxical. Why should this be?

Do not be misled by novelists who frequently invent improbable, exaggerated differences in their fictional conjoined twins in order to deliver a more exciting tale. Another paradox is that, in spite of differences, conjoined twins are forced by circumstance to live in harmony most of the time. Certainly the Hilton and McKoy twins did so. Indeed Dreger, in her book *One of Us: Conjoined Twins and the Future of Normal* (2004), wonders if we all might benefit from more twin-like behaviour. Whatever their nature, nurture and intentionality, the personality of conjoined twins must be affected by their inability to live independent lives.

To sum up, I suggest five influences that may tend to promote personality differences between twins, conjoined or not:

1. The interaction of nature and nurture with intentionality (free will) as described above.
2. Although MZ twins may be considered to share the same environment before birth, this is not always the case because some may not share an equal blood supply. This can result in one twin being born with too

much blood and the other with too little. The health of each may differ, even to the extent of the death of one or both (see Chapter 11).

3. In some cases, psychological differences can be due to the different anatomies of the twins. Conjoined twins frequently have differences in height, weight and other physical features, together with differences in intelligence. Indeed, one may have congenital anomalies which the other does not. Coping with a different type of body could affect personality.

4. Newman and others have argued that differences can be due to what they call 'asymmetry reversal'. MZ twins, whether conjoined or not, are more likely than DZ twins to have mirror-image characters. For example, left-handedness, fingerprints, dentitions and head-hair whorls have all been shown to be more common in MZ twins. Does this have any effect on personality? Probably not...

5. Could it be that non-conjoined MZ twins, when disagreeing, are better able to move apart, to be flexible, to seek compromise and so to move towards some measure of agreement, even to 'agree to differ' or to go their separate ways, rather than conjoined twins who are forced to stay close? The conjoined state could easily produce stress or tension, indicating individuality, but forcing compromise.

Although the studies described above tell us something about the psychology of twins we are left with an enigma: what do conjoined twins actually think and feel compared with the rest of us? Some of the time at least they may feel a sentimental attachment, such as is expressed in the Cole Porter song: "I've got you under my skin/ I've got you deep in the heart of me/

So deep in my heart/ You're really a part of me…" Was Porter thinking of twins or even of conjoined twins when he wrote those words? It sounds like it.

The Bunker twins seem to have led reasonably contented lives. Their marriages, their work, especially their farm work, and their children probably provided satisfaction in spite of their physical difficulties. They had refused separation when it was offered. The Hilton twins had adventurous lives with plenty of problems as well as pleasure.

Consider the words of Reba Schappell during a BBC interview: "You have to look at how the individual who is set conjoined perceives themselves. If you perceive yourself positive the public will look at you positive. Maybe it will take a while but even if the public doesn't look at you positive, if you're positive enough you're not going to give a hoot… You're going to like yourself the way you are. Do you, do you understand…? I hope the public out there does understand this."

Do these experiences confirm Dreger's assessment that, "… the desire to remain together is so widespread among communicating conjoined twins as to be practically universal".

On the other hand, the Bijani twins (see Chapter 6) decided on dangerous separation surgery in spite of their considerable successes in life: they had both qualified as lawyers. They knew the risk of failure, which sadly actually happened.

It is because of the statements of twins such as Reba Schappell that Dreger has expressed the opinion that, when possible, there is something to be said for letting twins make their own decision regarding separation when they are old enough to do so.

We can learn from the lives and opinions of people today who have physical or psychological handicaps. Many of them (most?) learn to adapt to their problems and to overcome them to some extent. Also there are many who enjoy Paralympic sports. So it is with surviving conjoined twins: they have no other option but to adapt to their circumstances; indeed, so do we all. Human beings are remarkably adaptable, especially those who can exploit and develop the power of mind over matter.

One of the most inspiring examples was the deaf/blind Helen Keller (1880–1968), who affirmed, "The best and most beautiful things in the world cannot be seen or even touched – they must be felt with the heart."

Chapter 14

Mythology

Throughout history, conjoined twins have appeared in myths and legends, in both human and animal form. There are also several mythical multi-headed creatures. Wikipedia lists about 130 mythological creatures with hybrid bodies which could be considered analogous to conjoined humans. Some of the best-known examples appear in Greek mythology and are described here. They are testimony to the extravagant possibilities of human imagination.

Lilith

There are numerous stories about Lilith. The rabbinical myths say that she was Adam's first wife. Another story is that God created Adam and Lilith as twins joined together at the back, like conjoined twins. It has been suggested that she is referred to in the book of Isaiah (34.14).

Hydra

Hydra was a serpentine water monster in Greek and Roman mythology. It had up to a hundred heads although some say only nine. It grew two heads when one was cut off. If the necks were burned, two new heads would not grow. The monster was killed by Heracles (Hercules) using sword and fire. This was one of twelve tasks Heracles had to perform on becoming the servant of Eurystheus.

Hecate

A goddess, often depicted in triple form, and sometimes regarded as the Goddess of Witchcraft. In Egyptian-inspired Greek esoteric writings and in magical papyri of late antiquity she is described as having three heads: one dog, one serpent and one horse. In other representations, her animal heads include those of a cow and a boar. Hecate's form is elsewhere expressed in a more Hellenic fashion in the vast frieze of the great Pergamon Altar, now in Berlin, where she is shown with three bodies taking part in a battle with the Titans. She is a character in Shakespeare's *Macbeth*. Macbeth refers to her in his dagger speech (Act II Scene I): "witchcraft celebrates pale Hecate's offerings". Later on (Act III Scene V), Hecate meets the three witches and demands to know why she has been excluded from their meetings with Macbeth. She is of continuing interest to present-day neopaganism.

Chimera

Chimera was, according to Greek mythology, a monstrous fire-breathing hybrid creature of Lycia in Asia Minor composed of the parts of more than one animal. It is usually depicted as a lion, with the head of a goat arising from its back and a tail that might end with a snake's head, and was one of the offspring of Typhon and Echidna and a sibling of such monsters as Cerberus and the Lernaean Hydra. The Chimera was finally defeated by Bellerophon, with the help of Pegasus, at the command of King Iobates of Lycia. Since Pegasus could fly, Bellerophon shot the Chimera from the air, safe from her heads and breath. Another account adds that he finished her off by equipping his spear with a lump of lead that melted when exposed to the Chimera's fiery breath and consequently killed her.

Orthrus
Orthrus was a two-headed dog owned by Geryon. In Greek mythology it guarded Geryon's cattle and was killed by Heracles. It was the offspring of the monsters Echidna and Typhon, and the brother of Cerberus, who was also a multi-headed guard dog. It was sometimes depicted with the heads of a goat and a lion and the tail of a snake.

Molionides twins
The twins were mythological conjoined twins called Cteatus and Eurytus. They had two complete bodies joined together, rather like the Bunker twins. They had two fathers, Actor and Moliona, and were reputed to be formidable fighters. After a great battle in which the twins defeated the army of Hercules, a truce was proclaimed. When the twins turned up for negotiations, Hercules set an ambush and killed them.

Janus
Janus had two faces, one looking forwards and one looking back. Although not normally referred to as a conjoined twin, he (they) has that appearance. The first month of the year is named after him. In January, we look back at the last year and forward to the next, and so the name is appropriate. Janus kept the Gate of Heaven, so he became the God of Doors and a door can let you in or out. He was very important, because a house is only as strong as its doors. His temple in Rome had

its doors thrown open in times of war, and closed in times of peace. They were usually open! The Emperor Augustus closed the doors of the temple, since he brought peace to the Roman Empire. A kind of conjoined twin in whom two bodies are joined at the head with two faces has been called Janiceps twins.

Double-headed eagle

The double-headed eagle, an obvious conjoined twin, is a common symbol in heraldry and vexillology. It has great antiquity, having first appeared in the Sumerian civilisation, many centuries BCE.

It is most commonly associated with the Holy Roman Empire and the Byzantine Empire. In the latter, the heads represent the dual sovereignty of the Emperor (secular and religious) and/or the dominance of the Byzantine Emperors over both East and West. However, the design was in use in the East for centuries before it was officially adopted by the Byzantines, and was independently adopted as the symbol of several other historical states.

More recently, it has appeared on the flag or coat of arms, past or present, of many countries, including Russia, Albania, Serbia, Germany and Spain.

Dionysus

Dionysus was allegedly born from the thigh of Zeus, thus resembling a parasitic conjoined twin. His mother was a mortal woman, Semele, and his father was Zeus, the King of the Gods. Zeus's wife, Hera, discovered the affair while Semele was pregnant. Appearing as an old crone, Hera befriended Semele, who confided in her that Zeus was the actual father of the baby in her womb. Semele demanded of Zeus that he reveal himself in all his glory as proof of his godhood. Although Zeus begged her not to ask this, she persisted and he agreed. Therefore he came to her wreathed in bolts of lightning; mortals, however, could not look upon an undisguised god without dying, and she perished in the ensuing blaze. Zeus rescued the fetal Dionysus by sewing him into his thigh. A few months later, Dionysus was born on Mount Pramnos on the island of Ikaria, where Zeus went to release the now fully grown baby from his thigh.

Dionysus is the Greek God of Wine and Fertility, the god who inspires ritual madness, joyful worship and ecstasy, carnivals and celebration. He was also known as Bacchus, the name adopted by the Romans.

Cerberus

In Roman and Greek mythology, Cerberus is a dog, usually with three heads, which guards the underworld to prevent escapes. He features in many works of literature, art and architecture. He is supposed to have been the offspring of Echidna, a half-woman and half-serpent, and Typhon, a fire-breathing giant. King Eurystheus ordered Hercules, as his twelfth task, to capture Cerberus alive. He did so, but the King was so frightened that he asked Hercules to return it to the underworld.

Cerberus features in Virgil's *Aeneid*, Plato's *Symposium* and Homer's *Iliad*. In Dante's *Inferno*, the dog tears to pieces those who are guilty of gluttony. In Milton's *Paradise Lost*, there is reference to Cerberean hounds in Hell. Some sculptures and vases show a two-headed dog. One of the earliest depictions is a Laconian vase from 560 BCE. A modern sculpture guards the entrance to the Royal Institute of Technology in Stockholm. A three-headed dog appears in *Harry Potter and the Philosopher's Stone*.

Legends

There exists a legend in Samoa of twin girls involving a mythological separation surgery. They were joined together by their backs. After many years (the girls had grown up) they were startled in their sleep and rushed from the house, each one by a separate door. The doorpost separated their bodies so that they were parted asunder.

A legend from Papua tells of a boy who was the foster son of "twin women who were joined fast together, flesh and bone, by the buttocks..." so that, "... when they would walk, the one must go forward and the other backward..." The boy saw how awkwardly the two women were joined together, "so while they slept at night, he took a bamboo and prised a sliver off it, with an edge sharper than any knife, and so neatly cut away the one from the other that both slept soundly the while, feeling no pain, and in the morning got to their feet, two separate women".

Chapter 15

Fiction and entertainment

Books

The Corsican Brothers by Alexandre Dumas (1802–1870)
Published 1844. English translation from French. Republished 2018.

This is a short novel (or long short story) based in Corsica and Paris. Conjoined twins and ghosts provide a charming tale with a clever plot. At least eight films have been made from this book, together with a television version in 1985. It provides an interesting commentary on Corsican society in the nineteenth century.

Mark Twain's books

Mark Twain (1835–1910), a contemporary of the Bunker, Tocci and McKoy twins, was so fascinated by them that he was inspired to write a mixture of fact and fiction about conjoined twins.

His first effort was an article entitled 'Personal Habits of the Siamese Twins', which appeared in *Packard's Monthly* in

1869 and was reprinted many times. This lampoons the Bunker twins with the aid of a good deal of fantasy. He has them on opposite sides in the American Civil War. Both are captured and both prisoners are exchanged! It has been suggested that this piece is a parody of the reconciliatory feelings of that time, or a cautionary tale, the Civil War having finished only four years before, and the United States needing to live up to its name. Chang is a total abstainer, whereas Eng gets drunk and the alcohol passes to Chang, thus making him drunk also. Eng is a Baptist whereas Chang is a Roman Catholic. When Eng is baptised, Chang agrees to be baptised also so long as it does not count. Chang wants to propose marriage to his lover but cannot do so while Eng is present. Eventually he manages it while Eng is asleep. One day they have a fight but neighbours are unable to stop them. An illustration by Rue Williams accompanied a publication in 1875. The piece is humorous but hardly in good taste as the Bunkers were still alive at the time.

In 1892, Twain wrote *Those Extraordinary Twins*, a tale of conjoined twins called Luigi and Angelo Capello, which was almost certainly based on the Italian Tocci brothers. He stated that he had seen a picture of an Italian 'freak' with two heads and four arms and a single pair of legs. He may have seen this in Italy. While writing this tale, other ideas and characters came into his mind which he eventually decided should be incorporated into a completely new book called *Pudd'nhead Wilson*. So, to quote Twain's own words, "I dug out the farce [meaning *Those Extraordinary Twins*] and left the tragedy." When this book was published in the USA it included *Those Extraordinary Twins* as an appendix.

In *Pudd'nhead Wilson*, the twins are not conjoined but instead are two boys born on the same day, one white and the other one-sixteenth black, who are accidentally swapped. One might even consider this tale to be a literary separation of conjoined twins. It provides a good tale which constitutes a scathing condemnation of slavery and race relations in the American South. Incidentally, the book also originated the term 'sold down the river', meaning a black person sold down the Mississippi to the slave-owning South.

The Siamese Twins: A Satirical Tale of the Times by Edward G. E. L. Bulwer (1803–1873)
Bulwer was an English novelist, poet, playwright and politician. He was immensely popular with the reading public and wrote a stream of best-selling novels, which earnt him a considerable fortune. He coined the phrases 'the great unwashed', 'pursuit of the almighty dollar' and 'the pen is mightier than the sword'.

This 311-page poem about the Bunker twins was written when they were aged only twenty. It is a mixture of fact and fiction. It is brilliantly written with amusing but stylish illustrations. Examples of the factual part of the poem have been quoted in Chapter 2. The major fiction recounted is that the twins were separated:

> *And the long bond was broken there!*
> *Apart were those, who from their birth*
>
> *As with one breast, the storms of earth.*
> *Yet ever differing, and disjoined*
>
> *Re-born – and with their common kind*
> *Made as their fellows…*

Nabokov's Dozen by Vladimir Nabokov (1950)
One of these thirteen short stories by the author of *Lolita* is entitled 'Scenes from the Life of a Double Monster'. The narrative is written from the perspective of one of a pair of male conjoined

twins who are asked if they can recall the very first time either of them realised the peculiarity of their condition. Their grandfather exhibited them for money which they disliked so much that they tried to run away. Nabokov's writing suggests that he had a plausible insight into the possible feelings of such twins.

A Canticle for Leibowitz by Walter M. Miller Jr. (1960)
This is a science fiction story with the prominent involvement of the Roman Catholic Church. A nuclear explosion results in a serious injury to Abbot Zerchi, who was fleeing with the ciborium (a receptacle for the Eucharist). He lies under tons of rock and bones in the abbey's crypts. While dying he encounters Mrs Grales/Rachel, a tomato peddler with two heads who is also dying. Zerchi tries to baptise Rachel but she refuses and instead takes the ciborium and administers the Eucharist to him before he dies. The implication is that Rachel, like the Virgin Mary and Eve, is exempt from original sin.

'Petition' by John Barth (1968)
This is a short story originally published in *Esquire* in 1968 and subsequently in Barth's book *Lost in the Funhouse* in 1988. Told in the first person by one of conjoined men, it is a fanciful account of a petition to His Most Gracious Majesty Prajadhipok, Descendant of Buddha, etc. who is visiting the USA. The writer is attached in piggyback style to the back of his twin – an impossible situation in real life. He compares their plight to that of Chang and Eng Bunker, whom he envies. He has suffered greatly from the domination of his twin, who calls him his "monkey on his back". He is especially frustrated when they both fall in love with a lady contortionist who joins them in their theatrical escapades to form an act called 'The Eternal Triangle'.

Orphans of the Sky by Robert A. Heinlein (1975)

This is a science fiction novel in which Joe-Jim is a two-headed creature who proves to know more about the true universe than the apparently normal characters. Joe-Jim may have been the inspiration for Zaphod Beeblebrox in Douglas Adams's *The Hitchhiker's Guide to the Galaxy*.

Brothers of the Head by Brian Aldiss (1977)

This is a short novel about conjoined boys. They become world-famous pop stars for a short time and then descend into tragedy. Ian Pollock's cartoonish drawings effectively illuminate this bizarre tale, which depends on the twins' differences to an extent that would be unlikely with real conjoined twins (see p.226 for the film).

Attachments by Judith Rossner (1977)

The story is told by one of a couple of female friends who meet up with conjoined men. The storyteller is a devotee of Freud and her friend a devotee of Marx. The resulting *ménage à quatre* leads to intriguing adventures which analyse the complicated psychology of the situation, not least the sexual aspects.

The Hitchhiker's Guide to the Galaxy by Douglas Adams (1978)

There have been many versions of this tale. The original BBC Radio series of 1978 has subsequently spawned novels, a television series, stage and film adaptations and computer games. A character called Zaphod Beeblebrox has two heads and three arms. He is from a planet in the vicinity of Betelgeuse, and is a "semi-half-cousin" of Ford Prefect, with whom he "shares three of the same mothers". Because of "an accident with a contraceptive and a time machine", his direct paternal ancestors are also his direct descendants. Zaphod invented the drink known as the

Pan Galactic Gargle Blaster. He was voted "Worst Dressed Sentient Being in the Known Universe" seven consecutive times. He has been described as "The best Bang since the Big One".

The Secret Twin by Denise Gosliner Orenstein (2000)
This is a novel about a boy whose parasitic twin is surgically separated from him a few days after birth. He loses his parents at the age of four. This unusual and tragic beginning to his life results in strange behaviour in a life entwined with that of the enigmatic nurse who looks after him from the age of thirteen. He cannot forget his lost twin. As our hero reflects: "We are the rarest of human beings, thorapagus [joined at the chest], fixed, born sharing one heart. There was only one heart between us. I lived."

La Cucina [The Kitchen] by Lily Prior (2000)
This is a tale set in mafia-dominated rural Sicily in the early twentieth century where, as the author reveals, "no one survived a disappearance". It is a story about food and sex: the food is exquisite, the sex almost surreal. Conjoined twins born into this scenario provoke claims of bestiality, incest or could the Catholic parish priest be responsible? Later on our heroine (not one of the twins) has cause to declare that she has a "banquet of the senses". The reader is likely to agree but the conjoined twins turn out to have little significance to the plot.

Chang and Eng by Darin Strauss (2000)
This is Strauss's first novel, published in the USA and then in the UK in 2001, when it was described as "The International Bestseller". The tale is based on the Bunker twins but told in the first person as if by Eng. While based broadly on true

events of the Bunkers' lives, there are considerable deviations, which make for an interesting tale, especially with regard to their possible sex lives.

Strauss explained: "The story you have just read is both true and not true… the book in your hands hopes to be ruled a novel and not a history. Most of its people and situations result strictly from the imagination. Where I have discarded or finessed or invented the details of Chang and Eng's life, it was only to elbow the facts towards a novel's own idea of truth."

The book pleased reviewers. For example the *Financial Times* remarked that, "Strauss has produced a book which gets beyond the freak show of reportage to explore, in depth and with compassion, issues of union and separation, of individual identity, and of the ways in which humans share or protect their inner selves." It has been translated into French, German and other languages.

God's Fool by Mark Slouka (2002)
This story is also about the Bunker twins but is told from the viewpoint of Chang, thus providing a fascinating complement to Strauss's novel, which is told from Eng's viewpoint. This novel is also based broadly on true events of the Bunkers' lives but with considerable deviations and speculation, which make for another interesting tale. Slouka conjures up saucy events. Here is an example from when women crowd round the twins full of questions. "Shall we see if they are men?" she asked, then turned in the roar of laughing and clapping women, but already hands were upon us, pulling down our clothes." Another example: in Paris they are persuaded to court a lady of the night, who is so intrigued by their deformity that she deprives them both of their virginity without making a charge! Favourable review comments included, in *Time Out*, "Tender,

angry, and hopeful... a first novel of great style, power and ambition".

Neither Strauss nor Slouka shies away from speculating as to the sex lives of the Siamese twins. Given that the brothers were joined at the chest by a 5-inch-long band of flesh and were perpetually turned slightly towards one another, a great number of questions arise as to how conjugal visits were arranged with their wives. Very little biographical detail is available in this regard, but both Strauss and Slouka provide respectful, but detailed, fictional explorations. In *Chang and Eng*, Strauss emphasises Eng's disillusionment with his marriage to Adelaide, which nonetheless produced ten children, and his subsequent secret obsession with his brother's wife, Sarah. Slouka does not delve much into the Bunkers' married lives, focusing instead on Eng's fictitious – and crushingly tragic – affair with a French socialite.

It is difficult to judge which of these two novels is the best. *Chang and Eng* is a more or less straightforward historical novel. *God's Fool* is more discursive and (believe it or not) focuses less on the twins' conjoined predicament and more on what it means to be a slaveholder.

A reflection: With regard to both the above novels, although they are well written and entertaining, we may wonder whether it is a good idea to mix fact and fiction. One assumes that the main reason for historical novels is that they allow the use of conversation as well as fantasy. However, this popular practice does not exactly facilitate the serious study of history; in fact, it can encourage misinformation.

The Girls by Lori Lansens (2005)
This is an interesting novel about conjoined females joined at the head written as an autobiography by both twins, and in

fact as a duologue. The success of the novel depends however on the dissimilarities between the twins to an extent that is unlikely in real life.

Love Will Tear Us Apart by Tara McCarthy (2005)

This is a well-written, racy novel about beautiful female conjoined twins who become a famous singing and dancing pop duo. All seems well until they experience sexual desires and adventures. Severe tensions arise when one wants to perform solo and the other aspires to appear in *Playboy*! The story is told by a journalist who is engaged to write their biography but she becomes a major character in the story.

A Cabinet of Wonders by Renee Dodd (2006)

This is a novel set in the early nineteenth century in which conjoined females, joined at their sides, live and perform in a carnival. They have many adventures and conclude that it is "far better to be a freak in the carnival than to be a medical conundrum out in the world".

Half Life by Shelley Jackson (2006)

This is a science fiction novel about female conjoined twins, one of whom has been sleeping for twenty years. The other, wanting to be rid of her sleeping sister, seeks the Unity Foundation, a mysterious organisation that promises to make two into one. The *New York Times Book Review* described the book as "… quite complicated, a whirligig of futuristic constructs, elaborate adventures, Venn diagrams, black comedy, Boolean systems, hilarious send-ups of identity politics, lists, songs, and mad science… truly glorious".

Ludmila's Broken English by DBC Pierre (2006)
Pierre, a previous winner of the Man Booker Prize, has written a splendid novel about conjoined twin men who are separated at the age of thirty-three. Emerging from an institution, they are suddenly plunged into the wide world, where their differences of character produce bizarre developments, especially when one of them gets his first taste of sex. The result is hilarious.

Snakewoman of Little Egypt by Robert Hellenga (2010)
It had to come sometime! A novel featuring a conjoined twin animal. The snakewoman of this excellent novel is married (but subsequently divorced) to the pastor of a church called The Church of the Burning Bush with Signs Following. This Pentecostal sect believe that God protects believers from snake bites and from drinking poison, as promised in the Bible (see Mark 16.18). While investigating this congregation, a professor of anthropology, influenced by the frantic worship, is persuaded to forget his scientific status and, thinking himself protected, picks up a two-headed rattlesnake. This snake had been found by the pastor and added to the church's collection. The professor is bitten and nearly dies. His faith was not strong enough, believe the congregation, while their pastor prevents him from getting medical help.

The Purveyor by Karelia Stetz-Waters (2014)
In this novel, conjoined girls are brought up in an extreme fundamentalist Christian environment from which they eventually escape, ironically, via an attempt to kidnap them for the cause of prostitution. This long tale is a sometimes confused tangle of intrigue, crime, sex slavery and lesbian love with a dash of sado-masochism.

The Sex Lives of Siamese Twins by Irvine Welsh (2014)
Siamese twins come in and out of the story, briefly. They are
aged fifteen. They debate whether to allow separation surgery.
However, the book is not about their sex lives, rather it is about
murder and depravity, and about two strange women whose
lives and careers become entangled in the most impossibly
bizarre ways.

One by Sarah Crossan (2015)
This is a fictional story told in the first person by one of
conjoined girls, their names being Grace and Tippi. The
author explains that it is based on the experiences of real-
life twins, both living and dead. One feels that the author
shows considerable understanding and insight. The result is
a truly moving, realistic diary of what it is probably like to be
conjoined. Events are recorded but of most significance and
interest are Grace's descriptions of feelings, her opinions and
her philosophising. For example, she overhears a fellow pupil
say, "Being a Siamese twin has got to be the Worst Thing Ever."
Her response is to reflect on the many evils in the world and
she concludes, "I have never once thought that I would like to
swap my life for any belonging to those people whose lives are
steeped in tragedy. Because having a twin like Tippi is not 'The
Worst Thing Ever.'"

Although there are 430 pages, the text could easily have
taken up only about fifty because the items are interspersed
by spaces. At first this seems strange but perhaps one can
think of the gaps as the passing of time between the various
events and comments. Or perhaps the spaces are intended
to encourage us to pause and reflect. A truly charming and
thought-provoking novel containing both triumph and
tragedy.

Four-Legged Girl by Diane Seuss (2015)
This is a book of poems, one of which is called *Four-Legged Girl*, which referes to Myrtle Corbin (see Chapter 4).

Entertainment

Conjoined twins have often been involved in showbiz. Several examples have been described in this book. Some do so from choice, to earn a living or because they have an extrovert desire to show off or entertain. Others have been coerced by their families or carers in the hope of gaining a fortune. Some have been treated well and some badly. Some are just exhibited, especially if their deformity is gross. Others learn how to entertain using dance, song, musicianship or acting.

Such exhibition is much less common today but the question arises: What should our attitude be in civilised society? If we were confronted with an exhibition would we enter and pay to support the individual or would that be cruel voyeurism?

Games and toys

There are various games featuring two-headed creatures such as *Magic: The Gathering* and *Two-Headed Sliver*. The *Fallout* series of video games features two-headed cattle. In fact, one-headed cows are considered abnormal! The Pokémon toys include Dodue, Zweilous and Girafarig. A number of artefacts can be purchased from eBay.

Plays

Early Morning by Edward Bond
Edward Bond, born 1934, is a distinguished English
playwright. His play *Early Morning* features conjoined twin
boys. The English Stage Society first performed it at the Royal
Court Theatre in London on 31 March 1968. Later that
same year it was banned by the Lord Chamberlain (who had
such authority) but within a year the law was finally repealed
and the ban lapsed. The cast included Nigel Hawthorne
and Marianne Faithfull. It is a hilarious farce, bizarre and
surrealistic. Historic nineteenth-century characters have weird
adventures, including suicides, murders and cannibalism!
There are strong hints that Queen Victoria and Florence
Nightingale had a lesbian relationship! Queen Victoria's sons
include the conjoined twins George and Arthur. George shoots
himself dead. Arthur survives, with George's body gradually
disintegrating into a skeleton during the play. After the death
of Arthur, the twins are joined in heaven, where Prince Albert
cuts them apart even though the skeletal remains of George
still exist, in heaven!

In 1969, when the Royal Court was finally able to perform
Bond's work legally, it toured with the play and two of his
other plays in Europe, winning the Belgrade International
Theatre Festival prize.

Futureproof by Lynda Radley
Futureproof is a magical and deeply human play by Lynda
Radley performed at the Edinburgh Fringe in August 2011
at the Traverse Theatre. It was her first play for the Traverse,
and a Fringe First 2011 winner. The play is set in Riley's
Odditorium, a travelling freak show featuring conjoined twins
Lillie and Millie. The show's popularity is declining drastically

and so Riley devises a reinvention of his freaks to meet modern tastes.

National Examiner (1984)

This is a supermarket tabloid owned by the American Media Corporation. Like other tabloids, its contents have often been questioned, and it has been derided for its sensational style.

In December 1984 the *National Examiner* reported the case of a pretty fourteen-year-old conjoined twin girl who had become pregnant by her male twin. A Dr Singh had reported the case and the girl's name was Indira, suggesting that the twins were Indian. This must be sheer fantasy of course because conjoined twins are always of the same sex. The report was probably published to promote sales of the magazine.

Films

Freaks (1932)

In 1932 the successful film producer Tod Browning persuaded the Hilton twins (see Chapter 5) to appear in an MGM film called *Freaks* that featured a cast of real freaks. It is based on the short story 'Spurs' by Tod Robbins published in *Munseys Magazine*. The Hiltons appeared for only a few minutes and later regretted agreeing to take part. The 'goodies' are the freaks and the 'baddies' are the normal characters. Initially the freaks welcome a normal-bodied woman, who pretends to accept them all and so they shout with pleasure, "One of us, one of us." However, when the freaks realise that she is out to exploit them they turn her into a sideshow exhibit and are then able to shout "one of us" with a different meaning. The film proved to be a disaster. For example, the secretary of the Board of Review in Atlanta, Georgia described it as "loathsome, obscene, grotesque and bizarre". It was banned in the UK. After about six months MGM withdrew it. However, in 1994, *Freaks* was selected for preservation in the United States National Film Registry as being "culturally, historically, or aesthetically significant". A full description of the film can be found on Wikipedia. In 2004, Warner Home Video released it with a '15' certificate and a warning that it "contains strong horror". It is available for private showing in the EU only. I am surprised it has now become available. In spite of one's aversion to censorship I think the Atlanta reviewer had a point. Perhaps Warner thinks we are now more tolerant of such material. Are we? Should we be? *The Hollywood Reporter* called it an "outrageous onslaught upon the feelings, the senses, the brains and the stomachs of an audience". However, in 2015, Peter Bradshaw in *The Guardian* gave it five stars out of five, calling it a "macabre masterpiece… A unique film."

Chained for Life (1951)

In 1951 the Hilton twins, who had appeared in *Freaks*, went to Hollywood again to make another film, this time a much more respectable one without a cast of freaks. It was called *Chained for Life*, and directed by Harry L. Fraser. The Hiltons play the part of conjoined twins in the film, which is based on Mark Twain's short story *Those Extraordinary Twins*. In the film the twins are called Dorothy and Vivian Hamilton. It is fictional but includes episodes roughly based on the Hiltons' life, such as their showbiz experiences and Dorothy's difficulty in getting married. A publicity stunt is planned in which Dorothy will pretend to marry Andre, one of the other performers, who has a stage act with guns. The stunt is wildly successful in America and Europe. However, Dorothy falls in love with Andre and marries him. He deserts her after one day. The resulting publicity throughout the world gets out of hand. Vivian gets revenge by shooting Andre with his own gun. In the subsequent courtroom drama, Vivian is accused of murder. The judge has the dilemma of how to punish one twin without harming the other. He appeals to the film's audience to make their own decision. First shown in 1953, it was a flop and the distributer went bankrupt. Alpha Video Distributers in the USA issued it on DVD in 2004.

Twin Falls Idaho (1999)

This film was written in the USA by actual (but not conjoined) twins Michael and Mark Polish, who act the part of conjoined twins Blake and Francis Falls. Michael Polish is the director. The twins live a secluded life in a tatty hotel until they contact a call girl called Penny to help celebrate their birthday. She is initially repelled by their deformity and runs away, but later returns. A love affair ensues. The twins develop a need for separation when one of them falls ill. The film is a touching, sentimental tale of two love affairs: one between the twins and the other between one of them and the girl. It had favourable reviews including, from the *San Francisco Chronicle*, this comment: "A beautiful love story that wants to break your heart and probably will." It received awards at the Athens and Deauville Film Festivals. A DVD was issued in 2006.

Big Fish (2003)

This film was made in the USA based on a novel by Daniel Wallace. Directed by Tim Burton, it received many awards, including an Oscar nomination for the score. In this modern fairy tale, Albert Finney plays Edward Bloom, a notorious storyteller who claims to have met conjoined twins in the Far East called Ping and Jing. After Edward dies his son has a vision in which he discovers that the twins were not joined, this being an example of Albert's many exaggerated tales. A DVD is available.

Stuck On You (2003)

This is a comedy film directed by the Farrelly brothers. It is about a pair of conjoined twins, Walt and Bob, acted by Matt Damon and Greg Kinnear, with small but significant parts played by Cher and Meryl Streep. The twins use their unique deformity as a means of gaining acceptance and endeavour to live as normally as possible. Everything is going well until Walt follows his dream

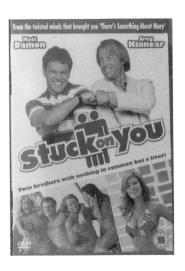

'Stuck on You' poster, film by Farrelly brothers. DVD issued 2004.

of making it as a Hollywood actor, and persuades his hesitant brother Bob to go along for the ride. The brothers also have to deal with the complications of dating as Bob meets and falls in love with May, a woman he met online, who is unaware that Bob has a conjoined twin. A DVD was issued in 2004.

Brothers of the Head (2005)

This is a film based on the 1977 novel by Brian Aldiss and was issued with an '18' certificate in the UK. The story concerns Tom and Barry Howes, conjoined twins. Their join is similar to that of the Bunker twins. They could have been divided but refused. They become highly successful music performers during the mid-1970s punk rock era in the UK. *Maxim* magazine called it, "One of the best British films in years."

Sisters (1973)

Sisters is a film written and directed by Brian De Palma, starring Margot Kidder and Jennifer Salt. It was released as *Blood Sisters* in the UK. The story centres on a news reporter who, after witnessing a murder, becomes involved in a criminal investigation surrounding a mysterious doctor and one of his former patients, a young French woman who is a separated twin. The director had been influenced by the Russian conjoined twins Masha and Dasha (see Chapter 7). The film had a troubled release history, and was never given a theatrical release. A remake directed by Douglas Buck was released in 2008.

Comics

EC Comics

Published in the USA, Siamese twins were a popular theme for EC Comics, appearing primarily in their three horror comics. No less than nine Siamese twin stories appeared in EC's horror and crime comics between 1950 and 1954.

Two Bad

Two Bad is a comic character who appeared as a toy and in comics, films and on the internet. Two Bad is a monster with two heads in the 'Monsters of the Universe' toy line accompanying the cartoon series. They were introduced in 1985, when they were called "the double-headed evil strategist". Their main characteristic is that the two heads are frequently arguing with each other. Originally, they were intended to be one good and one evil person. This plan gave way to them both being evil. The toy had spring-loaded arms that could bear-hug another creature, together with other movable parts. Several variations of the toy have been produced.

In the UK, Two Bad has featured in a comic series by London Editions. In this series, the heads still argue but they become clever inventors, producing for example the Buzz-Wheel of Destruction and the Crawl Bomb. However, in practice the inventions don't work, resulting in the heads blaming each other for the failures.

Musicals and song

Toronto Symphony Orchestra

In 1935 the Orchestra presented its first 'Christmas Box' concert. This was an annual event until 1957. Alongside a selection of Christmas music and carols, with which audience members could join in, the players gave original burlesque performances and presented skits. Stunt acts included the Sumvak Sisters, in which the violinists Elie Spivak and Harold Sumberg, dressed in a Siamese twin gown, performed on a single instrument, one fingering and the other bowing.

Side Show

A musical called *Side Show* (also called *Side by Side*), based on the life of the Hiltons, opened on Broadway in 1997. Lyrics were by Bill Russell. The twins were played by Alice Ripley and Emily Skinner. Music was by Henry Krieger. Vincent Canby of the *New York Times* commented, "Side Show is propelled and given emotional heft by the bright inventive score and lyrics…" Although it was nominated for, but did not win, four Tony Awards, including Best Musical, it only ran for ninety-one performances. The tale begins in a seedy sideshow with a rather unsavoury song: 'Come look at the Geeks', and later , they sing a sentimental but realistic showstopper: 'I will never leave you'

The show has had many revivals, including a 1999 Denver production by the Physically Handicapped Actors and Musical Artists League, and at Illinois in March 2008, with an abridged version being performed at Washington DC, also in 2008. A CD is available featuring the original Broadway cast.

Chang and Eng, The Musical

This Singaporean musical is based on the lives of the Bunkers. It was produced by Ekachai Uekrongtham, with music and lyrics by Ken Low from the book by Ming Wong. The musical was first performed in 1997, revived in subsequent years until 2002 and has since travelled around Asia. It became the first English language musical to be performed in the People's Republic of China, being staged between 9 and 11 December 1997 at the Century Theatre, Beijing.

The Return of the Two-Heided Man

This poem by Matt McGinn (1928–1977), a Glaswegian folk singer, songwriter, humourist and raconteur, was recited by him on an audio CD. The text is on a wall near The Two-Heided Man pub at 16 Hope Street in Glasgow, formerly known as McGinn's Bar.

> *A bunch of the girls were scoffing it up in the Saracen saloon.*
> *The kid that handled the music box was playing an old Scotch tune,*
> *"Why did you make me care?"*
> *At the back of the bar, as drunk as a lord, stood Dangerous Dan McCluskey,*
> *Eying up all the birds that were pouring them short measure whisky.*

When out of the night a two-heided man, wae a claw for a haun stumbled in.
He pulled a razor out of his pocket and said, "Where is the Twin?"
The lassies all fainted and Big Dan fled to fetch a Black Maria van.
Joe the Bull picked up his ears and said, "Don't tell there is another man?"

Well the two-heided man was insulted, and he told Joe the Bull tae "chuck it"
Joe bought him two pints of beer. Then put his razor back in his pocket.
Dangerous Dan was two minutes away and he came back with the van.
The polis came rushin' right in tae the place, they were after the two-heided man!

Well the two-heided man made a statement, and the polis they made a note of it.
The two-heided man was stuck up against two copies of Bible John's photokit.
The polis were liftin' the two-heided man when Joe the Bull showed their stupidity.
He was able to prove to the polis, it was a case of mistaken identity.

Television

Cat Dog
This is an American animated television series first aired between 1998 and 2001. The show follows the adventures of

Cat Dog, a hybrid of a cat and dog with two heads (one at either end of its single body) and no tail or hind legs. Because of their strange condition, Cat Dog are seen as outcasts in the city of Nearburg and are often harassed by the Greaser Dogs, a gang of rough thugs, and their neighbour, Winslow, a devious blue mouse.

Cat Dog: The Great Parent Mystery

This is a television movie made in 2001 based on the Cat Dog television series. Dog convinces Cat to go on a parent hunt. Along the way, they run into aliens, a sea monster, hillbillies and fire ants.

Futurama

This is an American adult animated science fiction sitcom created by Matt Groening for the Fox Broadcasting Company. The series follows the adventures of a late-twentieth-century New York City pizza delivery boy, Philip J. Fry, who, after being unwittingly cryogenically frozen for a thousand years, finds employment at Planet Express. In the third episode of the sixth production season there is a two-headed goat with heads on opposite sides of its body.

Amber Dhara

This is a Hindi language Indian television series that aired on Sony Entertainment Television from 2007 until 2008. The story revolves around the life of conjoined twins Amber and Dhara who share the vital organ, 'the liver', and are conjoined at the hip. Twenty per cent of the liver belongs to Amber's body and the remaining 80% belongs to Dhara's body, which rules out the possibility of surgery being carried out to separate the twins without killing one of them.

Hoaxes, etc.

The famous nineteenth-century showman P. T. Barnum and other showmen in the USA were not averse to deceiving their public. For example, in the late 1800s, Adolph and Rudolph were false conjoined twins. Rudolph had tiny malformed legs which facilitated the deception, in which they seemed to have only two legs between them.

In the 1930s the Milton Sisters, a pair of supposedly conjoined twins often confused with the Hilton Sisters, shocked audiences by entering into a heated argument during a performance and then suddenly separating themselves from each other and exiting on opposite sides of the stage.

The famous silent film star Marguerite Clark (1883-1940) used a doll or infant to simulate a parasitic twin, although she was possibly intending to amuse rather than to deceive.

'Hermaphrodite conjoined twins. Male on left, female on right. Impossible in reality. Musée de l'érotisme, Paris (now closed).

Pasqual Piñón (1889–1929), known as "The Two-Headed Mexican", was a performer with the Sells-Floto Circus in the early 1900s. Piñón was discovered by a sideshow promoter, who had noticed that he had a large tumour on his forehead. The promoter had a fake face made of wax that he placed on the growth, allowing the claim that Piñón had two heads. Many years later, the circus manager paid to have the growth removed. While it is possible for a person to have two heads (the condition known as craniopagus parasiticus), with one head upside-down on top of the other, Piñón's 'second head' was oriented upright, like his actual head, thus proving it to be a hoax.

The novel *Downfall* by Per Olov Enquist features Piñón, although it portrays the story as factual.

An image of conjoined twins, one male and the other female, which is impossible in reality, used to be on show in a Paris museum (now closed).

Bizarre surgery

Nazi atrocities

Dr Josef Mengele, the notorious Nazi doctor, was so obsessed with twins that he performed cruel experiments on them in the Auschwitz concentration camp during World War II. One can imagine that he would have liked to get his hands on conjoined twins, which he never did. He devised an exceptionally bizarre and cruel operation, described by Vera Alexander, an eyewitness, in a Central Television (London) broadcast in October 1985. This is also described in the book *Mengele: The Complete Story* (2000) by Gerald Posner and John Ware.

Nazi cartoon.

Mengele surgically joined one twin to the other to construct the semblance of conjoined twins. Alexander related, "SS men came and took two children away. They were two of my pets, Tito and Nino. One of them was a hunchback. Two or three days later, an SS man brought them back in a terrible state. They had been cut. The hunchback was sewn to the other child back to back."

A Nazi cartoon appeared in 1927 based on conjoining.

Two-headed rat

In 2017 it was reported that an Italian neuroscientist called Dr Sergio Canavero, living in China, had successfully transplanted the head of one rat onto the other. Such two-headed rats live for an average of thirty-six hours. Canavero claimed that this was to prepare the way for human head transplantation. Tipu Aziz, Professor of Neurosurgery at Oxford University, declared that not only was the study unethical, it was also not new: similar operations were performed on dogs in the 1950s, and on monkeys in the 1970s. As for human head transplants, he observed, "it's too mad even to discuss".

Evelyn Evelyn

An audio CD was issued in 2010 apparently featuring songs by conjoined twins who have two heads, two arms and three legs, together with the work of other artists. Three of the tracks relate the twins' history. Their website claims that there have been public performances. All of this is plausible, but Wikipedia and www.wired.com explain that the twins are actually performed by Amanda Palmer and Jason Webley.

Probable fiction

Edward Mordrake (sometimes written 'Edward Mordake') was reportedly the nineteenth-century heir to an English peerage. He supposedly had an extra face on the back of his head which, if true, could have been a parasitic twin. Mordrake begged doctors to have his "demon head" removed because it whispered horrible things to him at night, but no doctor would attempt it. Mordrake committed suicide at the age of twenty-three. The description of Mordrake's condition is somewhat similar to those of Chang Tzu Ping and Pasqual Piñón.

Bibliography

Biography

Butler, J. (2000). *Masha and Dasha*, Bern München Wien, Scherz (in German).

Butler, J. (2017). *The Less You Know the Sounder You Sleep.* London: 4th Estate (about Masha and Dasha, mostly fact (in English)).

Fanning, L. (1995). *Separated Angels: Shannon and Megan, the Fanning Twins.* Naperville Ill.: Story Book Press.

Frost, L. (Ed.) (2009). *Conjoined Twins in Black and White: The Lives of Millie-Christine McKoy and Daisy and Violet Hilton.* Madison: University of Wisconsin Press.

Hunter, K. (1964). *Duet for a Lifetime: The Story of the Original Siamese Twins.* London: Michael Joseph.

Jensen, D. (2006). *The Lives and Loves of Daisy and Violet Hilton.* Berkeley: Ten Speed Press.

Landau, E. (1997). *Joined at Birth: The Lives of Conjoined Twins.* Franklin Watts Library Edition.

Lindfors, Bernth. (2014). *Early African Entertainments Abroad.* University of Wisconsin Press.

Martell, J. (2000). *Millie-Christine: Fearfully and Wonderfully Made*. Winston-Salem: John F. Blair.

Orser, J. A. (2014). *The Lives of Chang and Eng: Siam's Twins in Nineteenth-Century America*. University of North Carolina Press.

Wallace, I. and Wallace, A. (1978). *The Two: A Biography*. New York: Simon & Schuster.

Wu, C. (2012). *Chang and Eng Reconnected*. Philadelphia: Temple University Press.

Other non-fiction

Bogdan, R. (1988). *Freak Show: Presenting Human Oddities for Amusement and Profit*. Chicago: University of Chicago.

Bondeson, J. (2000). *The Two-Headed Boy and Other Medical Marvels*. Ithace and London: Cornell University Press.

Bulmer, M. G. (1970). *The Biology of Twinning in Man*. Oxford: Clarendon Press.

Carson, B. (1990). *Gifted Hands*. Grand Rapids, Michigan: Zondervan.

Dreger, A. D. (2004). *One of Us: Conjoined Twins and the Future of Normal*. Cambridge, Mass.: Harvard University Press.

Drimmer, F. (1973). *Very Special People*. London: Amjon Publishers.

Fiedler, L. (1978). *Freaks, Myths and Images of the Secret Self*. Great Britain: Penguin.

Gaddis, V. and M. (1972). *The Glorious World of Twins*. New York: Hawthorn Books.

Gedda, L. (1961). *Twins in History and Science*. Springfield: Charles C. Thomas.

Gough, M. (1986). *Dioxin, Agent Orange.* New York: Plenum Press.

Gould, G. M. and Pyle, W. L. (1896/2010). *Anomalies and Curiosities of Medicine.* [NB. 2010 edition has no illustrations and no index]

Griffiths, P. J. (2003). *Agent Orange: Collateral Damage in Vietnam.*

Kilby, M., Baker, P., Critchley, H. and Field, D. (Eds.) (2006). *Multiple Pregnancy.* London: RCOG.

Leroi, A. M. (2005). *Mutants: On the Form, Varieties and Errors of the Human Body.* London: Harper Perennial.

Lindgren, L. (Ed.) (2007). *Mütter Museum: Historical Medical Photographs.* New York: Blast Books. London: Trolley.

MacGillivray, I., Campbell, D. M., Thompson, B. (Eds.) (1988). *Twinning and Twins.* London: John Wiley & Sons.

Machin, G. A. and Keith, L. G. (1999). *An Atlas of Multiple Pregnancy: Biology and Pathology.* New York: Parthenon.

Martins, E. A. (2012). *Agent Orange: History, Science, and the Politics of Uncertainty.* University of Massachusetts.

National Research Council. (2006). *Health Risks from Dioxin and Related Compounds.* Washington DC: National Academies Press. New York: Blast Books.

Newman, H. H., Freeman, F. N. and Holzinger, K. J. (Eds.) (1937, renewed 1965). *Twins: a Study of Heridity and Environment.* Chicago: University of Chicago.

Parker, J. N. and P. M. (Eds.) (2003) *Conjoined Twins: Medical Dictionary, Bibliography and Annotated Research Guide.* San Diego: Icon Health Publications.

Posner, G. L. and Ware, J. (2000). *Mengele: The Complete Story.* New York: Cooper Square Press.

Quigley, C. (2006). *Conjoined Twins: An Historical, Biological, and Ethical Issues Encyclopedia.* Jefferson, N. Carolina: McFarland & Co.

Segal, N. L. (2000). *Entwined Lives: Twins and What They Tell Us About Human Behavior:* Penguin Group.

Shields, J. (1962). *Monozygotic Twins: Brought Up Apart and Brought Up Together.* Oxford: Oxford University Press.

Slifer, D. (2000). *The Serpent and the Sacred Fire: Fertility Images in Southwest Rock Art.* Santa Fe, New Mexico: Museum of New Mexico Press.

Smith, J. D. (1988). *Psychological Profiles of Conjoined Twins: Heridity, Environment, and Identity.* New York: Praeger.

Spencer, R. (2003). *Conjoined Twins, Developmental Malformations and Clinical Implications.* Baltimore: Johns Hopkins University Press.

Worden, G. (2002). *Mütter Museum of the College of Physicians of Philadelphia.*

Fiction

Aldiss, B. W. (1977). *Brothers of the Head.* New York: Pierrot Publishing.

Bulwer, E. G. (1831). *The Siamese Twins: A Satirical Tale of the Times, with Other Poems.* London: British Library. (Fact and fiction)

Crossan, S. (2015). *One.* London: Bloomsbury Publishing.

Dodd, R. (2006). *A Cabinet of Wonders.* London: The Toby Press.

Dunn, K. (1989). *Geek Love.* London: Hamish Hamilton.

Jackson, S. (2006). *Half Life:* Harper Perennial.

Lansens, L. (2006). *The Girls.* London: Virago.

McCarthy, T. (2005). *Love Will Tear Us Apart.* New York: Downtown Press.

Nabokov, V. (1958). *Nabokov's Dozen.* London: Penguin.

Orenstein, D. G. (2007). *The Secret Twin.* Harper Tempest.

Paré, A. (1840). *Ambroise Paré on Monsters and Marvels*. Chicago: University of Chicago Press. (Mostly fiction)

Pierre, DBC (2006). *Ludmila's Broken English*. London: Faber and Faber.

Prior, L. (2000). *La Cucina*: Black Swan.

Purcell, Rosamond (1997). *Special Cases: Natural Anomalies and Historical Monsters*. San Francisco: Chronicle Books. (Semi-fiction)

Queen, E. (1933). *The Siamese Twin Mystery*. Glasgow: Hamlyn.

Slouka, M. (2002). *God's Fool*. London: Picador. (Fact and fiction)

Stetz-Waters, K. (2014). *The Purveyor*. Salinas, CA: Sapphire Books.

Strauss, D. (2001). *Chang and Eng*. London: Allison & Busby. (Semi-fiction)

Twain, M. (1894). *Pudd'nhead Wilson*. London: Penguin.

Verghese, A. (2010). *Cutting for Stone*. London: Vintage Books.

Welsh, I. (2014). *The Sex Lives of Siamese Twins*. London: Jonathan Cape.

Films (some are fiction)

Brothers of the Head (2007). Tartan DVD. *

Chained for Life (1951). Featuring the Hilton Sisters. Alpha video. Entertainment Inc. *

Face to Face: The Schappell Twins (1999). DVD. A&E Home Video.

Krivoshlyapova, *Masha/Dasha: 'Medical Documentary on Conjoined Twins'*. https://www.youtube.com/watch?v=MfDQKv2Ige0 (This is an edited version of the original Russian documentary, 16 minutes)

Side Show (1997). Original Broadway Cast. Video, DVD. Sony Music. *

Sisters (1973). A Brian De Palma Film. Cert 15. *

Stuck On You (2003). 20th Century Fox. Cert 15. *

Tod Browning's Freaks (1932). MGM film. Cert 15. *

Twin Falls Idaho (1998). A Polish Brothers film. Cert 15. *

BBC Horizon – Conjoined Twins (Broadcast 19.10.2000, 48 minutes)

* Fiction

There are several other films about conjoined twins available via the BBC item.

There are hundreds of published scientific papers, some of them available online including the one mentioned below. It describes one of the biggest studies as it is based on 383 examples from many countries:

Mutchinick O. M. et al. *Conjoined Twins: A Worldwide Collaborative Epidemiological Study of the International Clearinghouse for Birth Defects Surveillance and Research.* Am J Med Genet C Semin Med Genet. 2011 Nov 15; 0(4): 274-287.

About the Author

Michael L Cox was born and raised in Bristol and went on to qualify as a doctor at the University of Bristol. He met his wife as a medical student, and they went on to work at mission hospitals in Nigeria for seven years, which included the year of Nigerian Independence (1960) when Princess Alexandra, representing the Queen, visited the Queen Elizabeth Hospital, Umuahia where Michael showed her around. Three of his children were born at that hospital.

He eventually returned to England to specialise in obstetrics and gynaecology and continued his work at the George Eliot Hospital, Nuneaton until his retirement. At this hospital, conjoined twins were born under his care which stimulated interest and has resulted in this book, Born Together. He was also a founding member of the FSRH (Faculty of Sexual Reproductive Healthcare) and served on its council, started an IUCD (Intrauterine Contraceptive Device) clinic in Nuneaton and Vasectomy clinics in Leicestershire, on behalf of the Family Planning Association. He is still based in Nuneaton, Warwickshire and enjoys spending his time researching and writing.